Fabulous Fractions

Author
Judith Hillen

Editor
Betty Cordel

Illustrator
Reneé Mason

Desktop Publishers
Tracey Lieder
Leticia Hernandez

This book contains materials developed by the AIMS Education Foundation. **AIMS** (**A**ctivities **I**ntegrating **M**athematics and **S**cience) began in 1981 with a grant from the National Science Foundation. The non-profit AIMS Education Foundation publishes hands-on instructional materials (books and the quarterly magazine) that integrate curricular disciplines such as mathematics, science, language arts, and social studies. The Foundation sponsors a national program of professional development through which educators may gain both an understanding of the AIMS philosophy and expertise in teaching by integrated, hands-on methods.

ISBN **978-1-881434-82-5**

Printed in the United States of America

Author's Note:

It is with profound gratitude that I publicly acknowledge the many contributions and bountiful support from my AIMS colleagues including all the AIMS family at the home office. I am humbled by the expertise of AIMS Trainers across the nation who continue to provide staff development using these materials. This book is dedicated to them!

I Hear and I Forget,

I See and I Remember,

I Do and I Understand.

—Chinese Proverb

Table of Contents

Introduction/Overview

Fabulous Fractions is a collection of hands-on experiences that seeks to engage students in the use of manipulatives to develop concepts of fractions and equivalence. Students who have difficulties with fractions seem to operate on symbols without sufficient experience with concrete objects and events. With this in mind, every experience has been designed to help students build a concrete basis for their thinking about fractions and operations.

A variety of models are used extensively and fall into three basic groups: area models, linear models, and group or set models. The models then provide a way for students to build their own understanding of the meaning of fractions and of basic operations on them using these concrete materials.

Fabulous Fractions begins by examining issues related to why we teach fractions, how to connect our teaching to a learning model, and what directions are provided by national professional organizations such as NCTM. These big ideas form the basis upon which the experiences were designed and organized for this publication. Each model is supported with hands-on activities that provide opportunities for students to have multiple experiences with concrete materials and conversation with fellow students.

The design of each lesson includes purposeful attention to defining the **learning goals** which are then connected to two features: **evaluation** and **evidence**. Teachers and learners are encouraged to ask themselves—why am I doing this? And how will I know I understand? What is the evidence that could be provided and what is the accompanying explanation?

In addition to attention to the concepts of fraction equivalence and operations, there are a number of integrated activities that explore applications to problem solving, geometry, and data display and analysis.

Playful and intelligent practice is an integral part of this book and several card games are included that challenge students to apply their understanding of matching or pairing fractions to show equivalence or sums of ONE.

Fabulous Fractions concludes with a final word about fractions, an assessment experience with a scoring rubric, and a proposed checklist aligned with learning goals from each lesson.

Fraction Number Sense : Big Ideas

Meaningful and successful understanding of fractions includes these big ideas:

- a well-understood sense of fair shares

- an ability to recognize fractional numbers as equal (measured) parts of a whole and as equal (counted) parts of a group or collection of objects

- an understanding of the relative size of fractions and wholes

- an ability to recognize and name equivalent fractions

- recognition that in the symbolic representation of a fraction the numerator indicates how many parts of the whole are being considered, and the denominator indicates the size of the parts counted in the numerator or the number of parts in the whole where the whole is a set

- experience with operations on fractions using manipulatives in problem-solving settings

Fraction Number Sense : What is a FRACTION?

A fraction is an expression of a relationship between a part and a whole. The idea that a fraction is completely relative to understanding the nature of the whole as well as its parts is critical. Therefore, a significant amount of time must be dedicated to multiple experiences with models to develop this idea before students encounter pencil-and-paper computation of fractions.

Four kinds of models are explored in this book. They include:

- area models that employ a variety of geometric shapes such as a circle, a square, a set of pattern blocks, or Tangrams;
- length or number line models such as a ruler or other linear measuring tool;
- group or set models that include a collection of objects or groups of people; and
- a coordinate plane.

Fraction Number Sense : Why study FRACTIONS?

It is suggested in the NCTM *Curriculum Standards* that the value of studying fractions has **more** to do with the development of meaning for fractions as parts of a whole and of relationships among parts and wholes and **less** to do with paper-and-pencil computation. After all, when was the last time you penciled out a fraction computation outside the classroom? Far more important has been your ability to mentally compute and estimate results in problem-solving contexts. It may also be noted that some of the same patterns and ideas in the study of fractions may be translated from numbers to algebraic symbols.

FRACTION NUMBER SENSE : Model of MATHEMATICS

The development of the mathematical experiences in *Fabulous Fractions* is consistent with the belief that all learning takes place in four basic environments embodied in the Model of Mathematics. If students are to understand and appreciate their experiences with fractions, they must acquire and process knowledge in each of the four environments pictured and described here.

A MODEL OF MATHEMATICS

The circle represents hands-on activities that include the use of manipulatives and models such as circles and sectors, fraction squares, pattern blocks, Tangrams, paper rulers an fringe. These models provide opportunities for concept develop-ment, connections to algorithms, and interactive discourse among learners and teachers that contributes to deeper understanding.

The triangle represents mathematics in oral and written forms using the symbols to represent fraction concepts, relationships, and operations. Because of the unique representation of fractions with a numerator and a denominator, it is crucial that meaning be developed through the use of manipulatives.

REAL-WORLD EXPERIENCES — Doing

Counting
Measuring

Writing — **ORAL AND WRITTEN COMMUNICATION**

PICTORIAL OR GRAPHIC COMMUNICATION — Illustrating

CRITICAL THINKING — Thinking — N = ?

The square sym-bolizes the picturing of information and for many students is the most power-ful tool for solving basic operations or story problems. Pictures of area models such as the circle or the square can be re-created by students as a means to solving new problems. They provide a mental picture from which they can remember and use what they know and understand.

The hexagon represents the fourth environment in which there is oppor-tunity to reflect about the actions that have been performed or observed. In this set-ting both the teacher and the learner are engaged in critical thinking, analysis, gen-eralizing and applications to new settings.

Our best teaching and learning comes from the many connections and translations among these four environments. The model provides a way to design both instruction and evaluation.

FRACTION NUMBER SENSE : Addressed in NCTM STANDARDS 2000*

- *Develop understanding of fractions as parts of unit wholes, as parts of a collection, as locations on number lines, and as divisions of whole numbers*
- *Use models, benchmarks, and equivalent forms to judge the size of fractions*
- *Recognize and generate equivalent forms of commonly used fractions, decimals, and percents*
- *Develop and use strategies to estimate computations involving fractions and decimals in situations relevant to students' experience*
- *Use visual models, benchmarks, and equivalent forms to add and subtract commonly used fractions and decimals*
- *Work flexibly with fractions, decimals, and percents to solve problems*
- *Compare and order fractions, decimals, and percents efficiently and find their approximate locations on a number line*
- *Understand the meaning and effects of arithmetic operations with fractions, decimals, and integers*
- *Select appropriate methods and tools for computing with fractions and decimals from among mental computation, estimation, calculators or computers, and paper and pencil, depending on the situation, and apply the selected methods*
- *Develop and analyze algorithms for computing with fractions, decimals, and integers and develop fluency in their use*
- *Develop, analyze, and explain methods for solving problems involving proportions, such as scaling and finding equivalent ratios*

* Reprinted with permission from *Principles and Standards for School Mathematics,* 2000 by the National Council of Teachers of Mathematics. All rights reserved.

Seeing FRACTIONS Among Ourselves

Topic
Fractions
    Group/Set Model

Learning Goals
- To recognize and name fractions as representative of a counted part of a group or set of objects
- To understand the meaning of numerator and denominator in the symbolic form of a fraction

Guiding Document
NCTM Standard 2000*
- *Develop understanding of fractions as parts of unit wholes, as parts of a collection, as locations on number lines, and as divisions of whole numbers*

Materials
For each group of 3-6 students:
    one sheet of chart paper
    colored marking pens

Background Information
    A group of people or a set of objects may represent a whole and any part of the group or set may be expressed as a fraction where the denominator represents the total number in the group or set and the numerator represents the number or part of the set that shares a common attribute or characteristic being described. The size of the group is a counted number. In other fraction models, size is determined by a measured number.

Procedure
1. Distribute colored marking pens and chart paper to each group of 3-6 students.
2. Explain that each group will be illustrating themselves and calling attention to special characteristics that they may have in common with each other.
3. In small groups, have students observe and discuss features and attributes of each member paying attention to those that are in common among the group. Attributes should be observable or verifiable through discussion. For instance, wearing glasses or a watch is observable. Having a cat or dog for a pet is verifiable through conversation.

4. On chart paper, direct students to draw simple stick figures to represent each person in their group.
5. Have them write five true statements about the group using fractions to express what they have observed.
6. Tell them to illustrate each statement by exaggerating the attribute or characteristic featured. For example:

7. Advise students to be prepared to share with the class their discoveries and observations and to participate in class discussion.

Discussion
1. How are all the fractions alike? [same denominator] Why is this so? [The denominator tells how many are counted in the whole group. Denominator also comes from Latin "de nom" and means to give a name.]
2. How are some of the fractions different? [different numerators] Why is this the case? [Numerator comes from the Latin that means number and the numerator tells how many share one attribute.]
3. When the denominators of several fractions are the same, what do you know about the groups or sets of objects represented? [They are the same size or number.]
4. When the numerators of several fractions are the same, but the denominators are different, such as $\frac{2}{3}$ and $\frac{2}{5}$, what do you know about the groups or sets represented? [The groups are different sizes but the number of objects sharing a common attribute are the same in each set.]

5. How does the shadow fraction or complement of each part of a group relate to the whole? [$\frac{2}{5}$ are wearing watches; $\frac{3}{5}$ are not.]

Evaluation

Display picture of a group of six. See *Group Pictures You Can Count On.*

Group evaluation

Picture may be enlarged for group evaluation. Each student writes **one** fraction sentence describing an observed characteristic in the picture. Post number sentences on the board.

Independent evaluation

If used as an independent evaluation or as an extended experience at home, duplicate the picture as is and have each student write five fraction sentences about the picture.

Evidence of Learning

1. Look for accurate representation of numerator and denominator connected to the picture.
2. Listen for appropriate explanation of reasoning in response to class discussion.
3. Ask for an example of a fraction in the real world that shows understanding of the meaning of numerator and denominator.

* Reprinted with permission from *Principles and Standards for School Mathematics,* 2000 by the National Council of Teachers of Mathematics. All rights reserved.

Write five (5) true statements using fractions to describe the group picture.

Think of another group of people or objects and write a fraction sentence that shows you understand the meaning of the numerator and denominator.

FRACTION SCAVENGER HUNT

Topic
Fractions
Group/Set model

Learning Goals
- To be able to illustrate in multiple ways how a given fraction can be represented as a part of a group or set of objects
- To heighten awareness of fractions in the real world

Guiding Document
NCTM Standard 2000*
- *Develop understanding of fractions as parts of unit wholes, as parts of a collection, as locations on number lines, and as divisions of whole numbers*

Materials
Colored marking pens or pencils
Large (12" x 18") white paper

Background Information
This activity may be used as an evaluation of student's understanding of symbolic representation of simple, everyday fractions such as $\frac{1}{2}, \frac{2}{3}, \frac{3}{4}$.

Management
This activity may be an independent activity for evaluation of understanding or a group/cooperative introductory lesson to gather multiple examples of groups or sets to illustrate fractions.

Procedure
1. Distribute one sheet of paper to each cooperative pair or group of students.
2. Have students fold the paper into four equal sections as pictured.

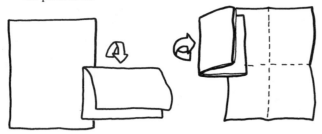

3. Invite the students to look for examples of fractions in the classroom, on the playground, or in their creative imagination of the real world.

4. Have them illustrate each example and be ready to explain how each picture accurately shows the meaning of the fraction in terms of fair shares, size or number in the group or set, and its relationship to the whole number one. Limit examples to fractions with denominators less than or equal to 12.
5. Alert them to be prepared to share their fraction finds with the class.

Discussion

1. How many different ways were you able to represent fractions? [many—potentially four times as many students]
2. What do all the fraction pictures have in common? [The size of the group or total number of objects matches the denominator of the fraction. The numerator of the fraction matches the number of objects being considered or talked about.]
3. Examine each picture to name the fraction that remains un-named. For instance, a picture that intends to illustrate $\frac{2}{3}$ shows three people and two of them are wearing hats, one-third is also shown because one of the three is NOT wearing a hat. Have students name both fractions that are illustrated in each picture.
4. Both fractions represent what? [the whole]
5. What other relationships did you observe or discover?

Evidence of Learning
1. Look for illustrations that appropriately picture the assigned fraction.
2. Listen for convincing explanations that describe a student's reasoning and creativity.
3. In what ways did students show insight beyond what you expected? (for instance, observe that $\frac{2}{4}$ is the same as $\frac{1}{2}$ or that $\frac{3}{4}$ is more than one-half)

* Reprinted with permission from *Principles and Standards for School Mathematics*, 2000 by the National Council of Teachers of Mathematics. All rights reserved.

Black Wholes And Bright Parts

Topic
Fractions
    circle/sector model
    part/whole relationships
    equivalence
    numerator/denominator
    comparing
    ordering
    addition
    subtraction

Learning Goals
- To understand concept of fair shares
- To understand relative size of fractions by direct comparison
- To recognize and name equivalent fractions
- To recognize fractional numbers as equal parts of a whole

Guiding Document
NCTM Standards 2000*
- *Develop understanding of fractions as parts of unit wholes, as parts of a collection, as locations on number lines, and as divisions of whole numbers*
- *Use models, benchmarks, and equivalent forms to judge the size of fractions*
- *Recognize and generate equivalent forms of commonly used fractions, decimals, and percents*
- *Use visual models, benchmarks, and equivalent forms to add and subtract commonly used fractions and decimals*
- *Compare and order fractions, decimals, and percents efficiently and find their approximate locations on a number line*
- *Understand the meaning and effects of arithmetic operations with fractions, decimals, and integers*

Materials
For each group of 3-4 students:
    one set of circles (6) on black construction paper
    one set of each fraction, each in a different, bright color:

12 halves	12 thirds
12 fourths	12 fifths
12 sixths	12 eighths
12 tenths	12 twelfths

    or one set of AIMS Fraction Circle Model

Background Information
The circle model has several advantages as the whole is easily defined and can always be reconstructed from any part because of the radius on both sides of any sector. This model is also helpful for students in illustrating addition or subtraction operations. Addition requires that parts be laid side by side in a circular fashion and renaming the sum of the parts. Subtraction requires that the portion to be subtracted overlaps or partially covers the initial fraction.

This lesson is exploratory and introductory in nature and the tasks described in the procedures are only suggestions which may be expanded by very creative teachers.

Management
1. The black wholes and bright parts may be cut from construction paper using the patterns provided or an Ellison die cut or Accu-Cut machine is very helpful and time efficient.
2. When students ask if they can write the name of the fraction on each piece, point out that you would rather that they *recognize* the relative size of the fraction rather than just *read* the name of the fraction. Therefore, try to discourage any writing on fraction pieces.
3. The procedures in this lesson are mixed with discussion questions because the lesson is primarily one of exploration and the questions are best "threaded" throughout the experience. Also included are references to activity pages in the event that a written record becomes useful for students and teachers to recall their learning and their thinking. Good teaching and learning require that we encourage students to ask questions of each other and their teacher while engaged in hands-on work with the manipulatives. Some of these questions may be predictable while others can be unanticipated. The discussion portion of this lesson includes some questions that help students to generalize their thinking.

Procedure
1. Distribute a set of fraction wholes and parts to each group of 3-4 students. Ask students to sort identical parts into sets. Most students will sort according to color and then recognize that all parts of one color are also the same size.

2. **Naming fractions.** Explore the idea with students that you would like to give each part that is a different color or size a fraction name. Inform them that they are to determine the name of all the different parts and be able to explain their thinking. It may be helpful to use the largest part, one-half to demonstrate that it takes two of those parts to completely cover the black whole without any gaps or overlaps. Emphasize that since it takes *two parts to cover*, two becomes the name of the denominator of the fraction. Inform them that the numerator is the number of pieces under consideration, in this case the one piece that you are pointing out.

3. **ONE is a big idea.** Direct the students to use congruent fraction pieces to cover the black whole by counting to get to ONE. Encourage them to try thirds, fourths, eighths, etc. See also *One is a Big Idea.*

4. Encourage discussion that connects the process of covering with a written record of denominator and numerator.

5. **Exploring mixed numbers.** Ask students to gather seven fourths. How many black wholes can you cover? How many left over? How do you make a record of that? (1 and $\frac{3}{4}$, or $\frac{7}{4}$) Have them try several others such as eight fifths, five thirds, 13 sixths, etc. Invite them to try reversing the process by showing one and $\frac{2}{3}$. How many thirds?

6. **Comparing fractions.** Ask students to use direct comparison of two fractions to determine which is the larger, smaller, or equal size fraction.

7. **Equivalent fractions.** (See *It's a Cover-Up.*) Have students show and describe all the ways to cover one-half with fair shares (identical pieces). How many? What size?

8. **Adding fractions.** Introduce addition and subtraction by asking students to find the sum of $\frac{1}{2}$ and $\frac{1}{3}$. Have them use the black whole and combine these unlike pieces. Direct them to find two ways to name the sum using the fraction circle parts. (Students may cover the black whole by placing the two unlike pieces side by side. Some will cover the colored parts of the circle with identical pieces and name the sum $\frac{5}{6}$. Others will fill in the empty or open place on the black whole and name the piece that is missing, $\frac{1}{6}$, and conclude that the sum must be ONE whole take away $\frac{1}{6}$. Both ways of thinking are to be commended.) No written record is made in this exploratory stage.

9. **Subtracting fractions.** Have students find $\frac{1}{2}$. Direct them to take $\frac{1}{3}$ away from $\frac{1}{2}$ by covering $\frac{1}{2}$ and naming the part that remains.

10. **Ordering fractions.** Name three, four or five fractions and ask students to place them in order from smallest to largest using direct comparison to verify their answers.

11. Ask students to order the fraction parts from largest to smallest. Trace and label each piece on a large (12" x 18") paper.

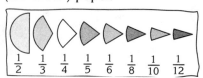

$\frac{1}{2}$ $\frac{1}{3}$ $\frac{1}{4}$ $\frac{1}{5}$ $\frac{1}{6}$ $\frac{1}{8}$ $\frac{1}{10}$ $\frac{1}{12}$

Discussion

1. What is the relationship of each of the brightly colored parts to the black circle? What does the circle represent? [one whole] How did each part get its name? [by covering the whole with identical parts, the number or how many it takes to cover describes the size of the part.]

2. How do the numerator and denominator relate to the circles and parts?

3. How can the bright parts have many names? Give an example that shows you understand equivalent fractions. Can all parts have other names? Why or why not? [The smallest parts do not have a smaller part to cover and rename, but theoretically it could be done.]

4. How many ways can you name the whole number ONE? Give three examples and explain your thinking.

5. What happens when the numerator (which tells how *many* parts) is larger than the corresponding denominator? How do we name this number? [mixed number, improper fraction]

6. Why is it that the larger the unit fraction (fractions with a numerator of one), the smaller the denominator? For example, explain why $\frac{1}{3}$ is larger than $\frac{1}{7}$. [Larger denominators mean more pieces, not greater size.]

7. How is it that fractions can have so many names?

Evaluation

Two activity pages, *One is a Big Idea* and *It's a Cover Up,* could provide on-going evaluation to better serve the teacher in making decisions about further instruction. They could provide clues to initial understanding.

Evidence of Learning

1. Listen for appropriate use of the language of fractions connected to students' explanations of fair shares and naming fractions.

2. Observe students' use of manipulatives in their explanations and problem solving.

3. Listen for questions and comments that show insight and deeper understanding.

4. Ask students to use the manipulatives (circles and parts) while they are explaining how to solve a problem.

* Reprinted with permission from *Principles and Standards for School Mathematics,* 2000 by the National Council of Teachers of Mathematics. All rights reserved.

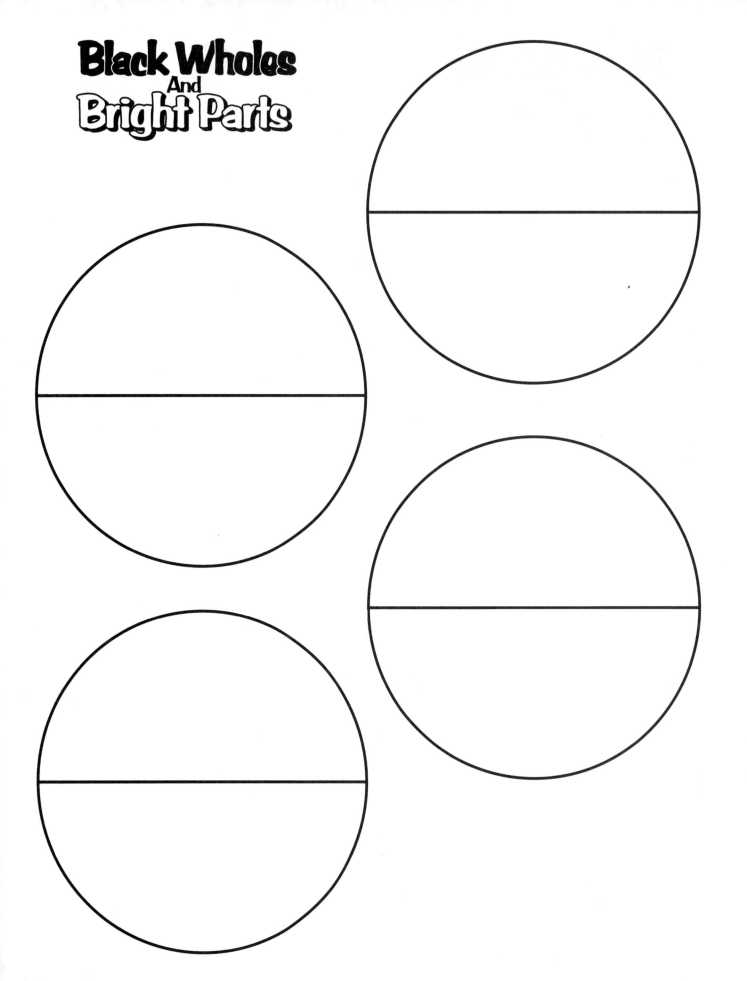

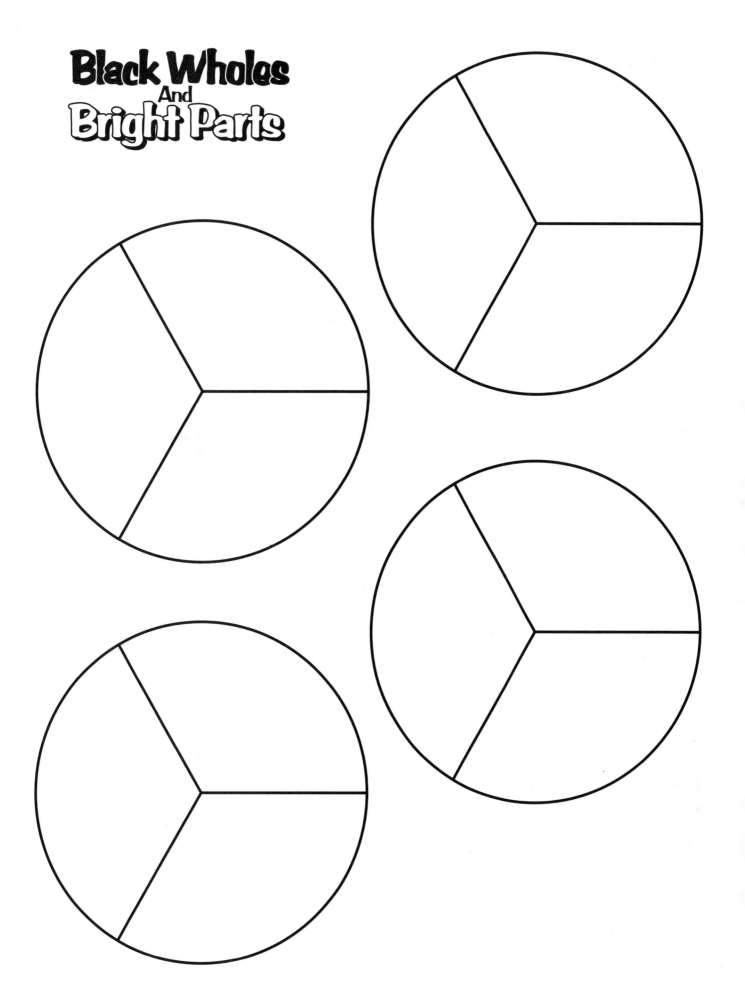

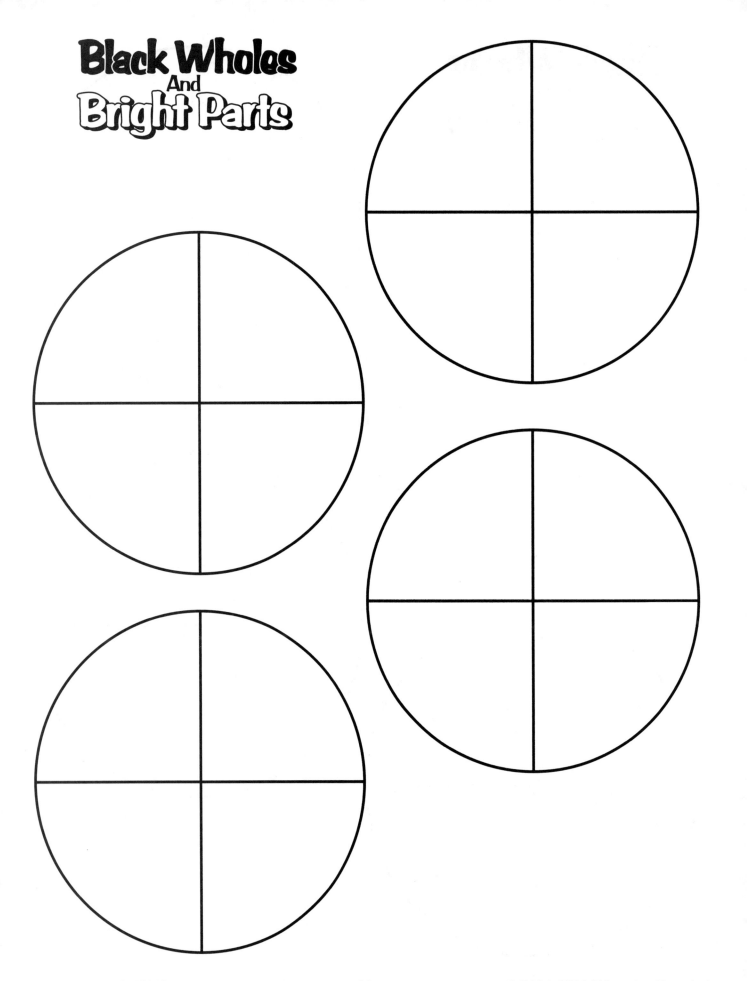

Black Wholes And Bright Parts

Black Wholes And Bright Parts

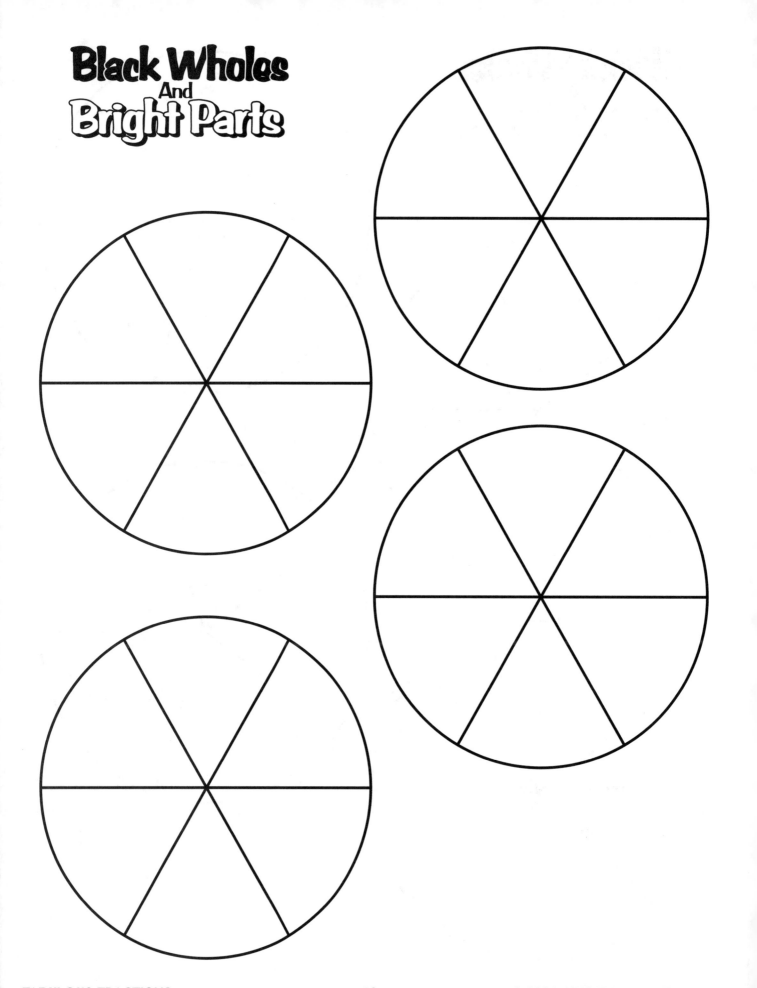

Black Wholes And Bright Parts

Black Wholes
And
Bright Parts

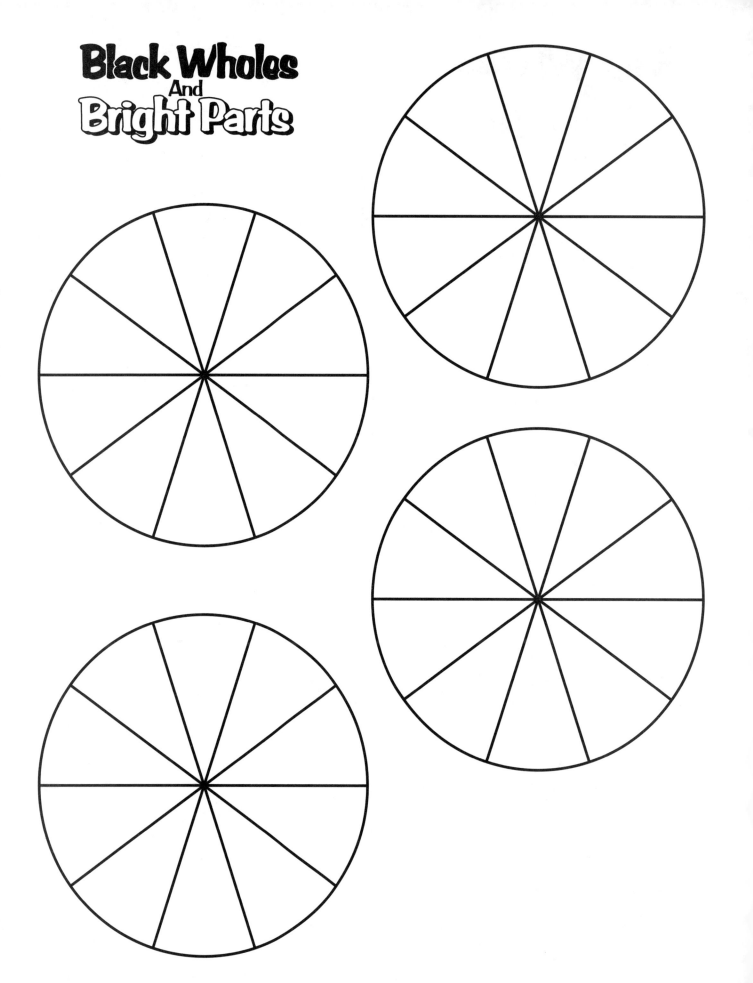

Black Wholes
And
Bright Parts

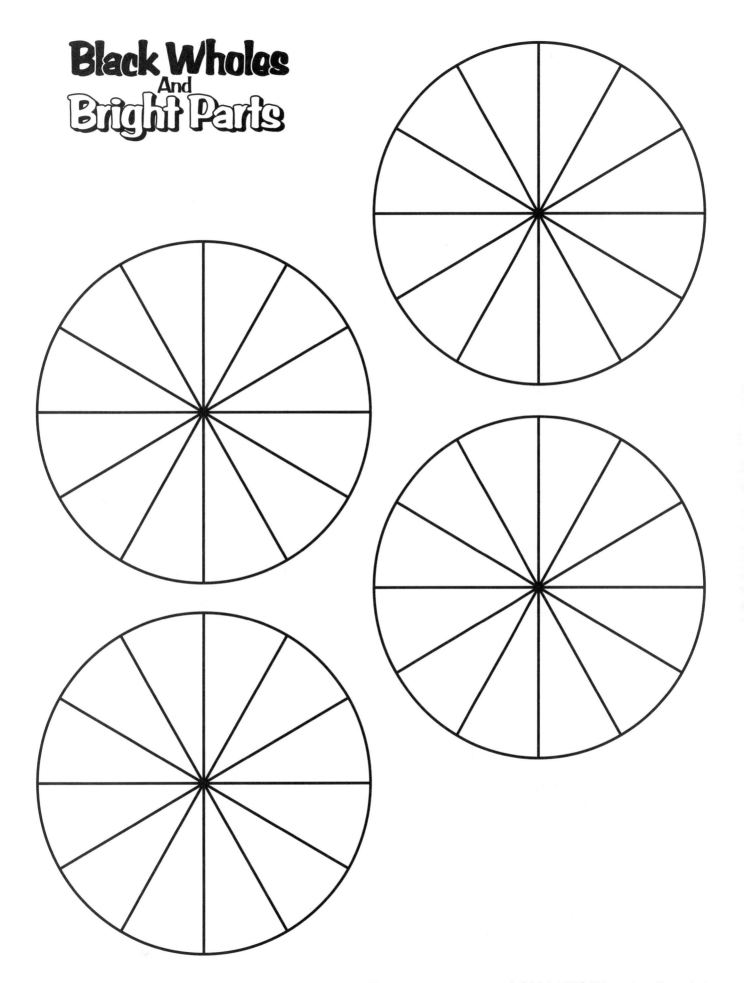

Black Wholes And Bright Parts

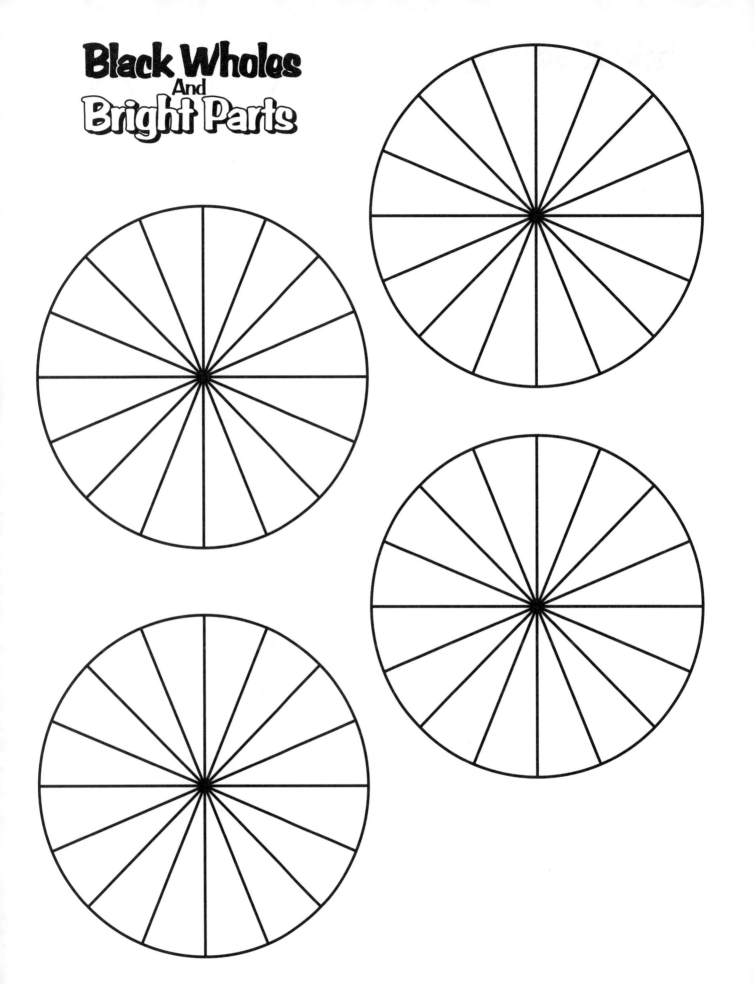

Use the "black whole" and identical circle parts to cover and find all the possible names for ONE. Make a record in such a way that the top number (numerator) tells how many it takes to cover the whole and the bottom number (denominator) tells the size of the circle part you are using. Fill in the circles to complete the picture.

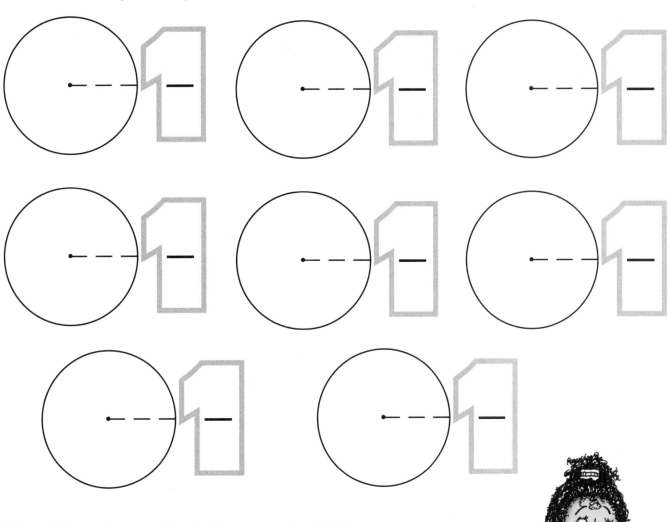

What did you discover about other names for ONE?

Give some examples for other names for ONE.

Black Wholes And Bright Parts :

It's a Cover-Up

Make a learning record of your discoveries.
Show and describe all the ways to cover one-half with fair shares. Include both a picture and the fraction equivalent.

One-half can be covered in these ways:

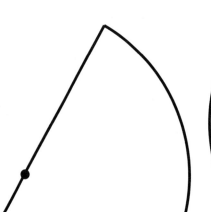

$\frac{1}{2}$ = _____

$\frac{1}{2}$ = _____

$\frac{1}{2}$ = _____

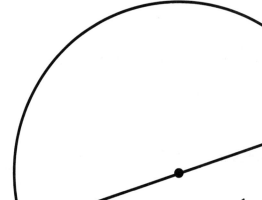

$\frac{1}{2}$ = _____

Show how other circle parts can be covered with fair shares. Use pictures and fractions to complete your work.

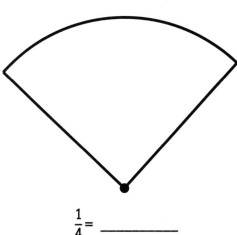

$\frac{1}{4}$ = _____

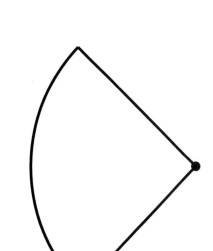

$\frac{1}{4}$ = _____

$\frac{1}{4}$ = _____

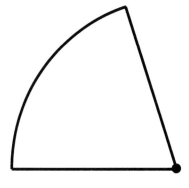

$\frac{1}{5}$ = _____

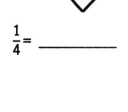

$\frac{1}{6}$ = _____

An interesting discovery or puzzling observation is this:

Topic
Fractions
Common Denominators

Learning Goals
- To construct and use a model that illustrates the meaning of common denominators
- To use the model to understand and practice addition and subtraction of like and unlike fractions

Guiding Document
NCTM Standards 2000*
- *Develop understanding of fractions as parts of unit wholes, as parts of a collection, as locations on number lines, and as divisions of whole numbers*
- *Use models, benchmarks, and equivalent forms to judge the size of fractions*
- *Recognize and generate equivalent forms of commonly used fractions, decimals, and percents*
- *Use visual models, benchmarks, and equivalent forms to add and subtract commonly used fractions and decimals*

Materials
Colored pencils
AIMS Fraction Circle Model

Background Information
Understanding the significance of using common denominators rests on understanding the concept of equivalent fractions. The important idea is that students can recognize that conceptually $\frac{3}{8}$ plus $\frac{2}{4}$ is the SAME problem as $\frac{3}{8}$ plus $\frac{4}{8}$ and that its written form has changed, using a common denominator, to facilitate a solution that can be named. Using the circle sector model to compare both forms of the problem is helpful.

Similarly, work with subtraction of unlike fractions, using the model to show how the unlike fractions are rewritten to make it easier to find a solution.

Some students may have trouble finding common denominators because they are not able to quickly come up with common multiples of the denominator. This is strong rationale for having a good command of the basic facts for multiplication—a skill that can be practiced.

It will be important for students to make a habit of looking at the denominators first to check to see if they are the same or different and then to be able to make good decisions about how to choose a common denominator that is most efficient.

Procedure
1. Distribute a *Sample CD* to each student and a set of circle models (or paper replica) to each pair of students.
2. Introduce the idea that this model will be used with a *Sample CD* to explore addition and subtraction of fractions.
3. Explain features of the CD: a center point and a dashed line that identifies the starting point and correct clockwise placement of fraction parts. Demonstrate that in this sample CD the students need to look at the big ONE at the top of the outside ring. The denominator in the big ONE indicates the name of the CD and the number of equal parts on the disk and thus serves as a Common Denominator (CD). Each fraction part is marked on the disk and has the same denominator. Suggest that students place $\frac{1}{4}$ in the CD model and observe the correct fraction name in the outside ring. Have them try placing $\frac{1}{3}$ and notice that it does not correspond to a mark and name on the outer ring. Emphasize the necessity for each fraction part to correspond to a mark on the outside ring. If it doesn't, the common denomination is not found on that disk. In the example above, 4 is not a common denominator for thirds.
4. Ask students to follow along as they are guided through the sample addition and subtraction problems suggested on the demo disk using the circle model and the CD.
5. Facilitate a discussion as appropriate incorporating questions suggested as well as questions posed by students.
6. When students seem ready, move on to *CD Practice* where students work more independently at four problems. It will be necessary to introduce four additional CDs for students' use. Distribute a set of CDs—6, 8, 10, and 12. Let students try selecting the appropriate CD for each problem and to work independently.
7. An additional page of *Collector's CDs* can be used for more complex problems with common denominator of 16 or 24. In the *Collector's CD*, fractions are in lowest terms. See *More CD Play* with additional problems.
8. Record equivalent fractions as you use CDs to solve the problems.

Discussion
1. What procedures did you use to add fractions with the same denominator? [add the numerators]

2. How did using the model help you understand adding fractions? [Answers will vary. Most will say that "seeing" the parts placed next to each other increased the area.]
3. Why and when is a common denominator necessary? [It is necessary for adding and subtracting unlike fractions because it provides a way to describe or name the result of the operation on unlike parts. For example, what is the name of the resulting sum when you add thirds and fourths?]
4. What number facts or operations are helpful in considering common denominators? [multiplication, division in looking for multiples and divisors]

Evaluation

The big idea here worth evaluating is the extent to which students are able to understand the meaning of a common denominator (conceptual) and an appropriate way to find one (procedural). A simple question could serve that purpose when suggested that an explanation be supported with either pictures or a manipulative. For example, ask students to explain why thirds go better with sixths than with fourths. Explain with words and pictures or a concrete model.

Another way to get at the same ideas would be simply to pose a problem of addition of unlike fractions and ask a student to solve the problem using manipulatives to support their thinking and explanation.

Evidence of Learning

1. Much of the evaluation of understanding will come from listening to students' explanations of their thinking.
2. Listen for validation of their thinking about common denominators, particularly with regard to the questions suggested under *Discussion*.

* Reprinted with permission from *Principles and Standards for School Mathematics,* 2000 by the National Council of Teachers of Mathematics. All rights reserved.

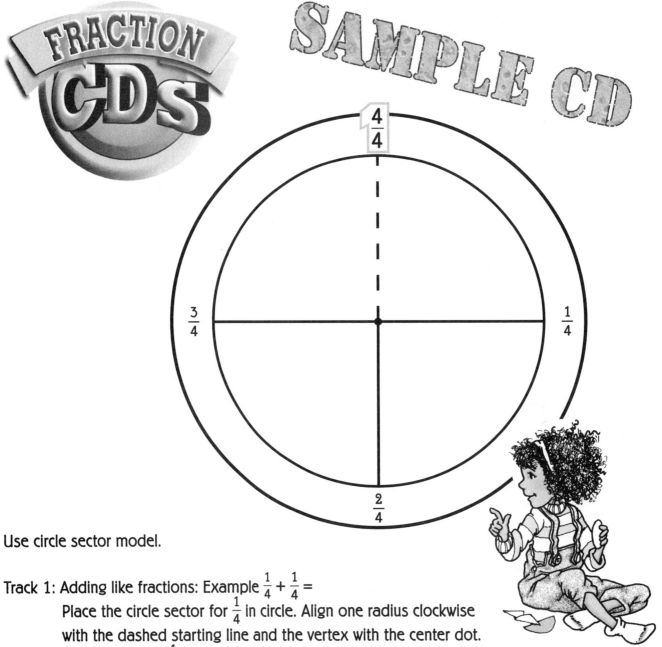

Use circle sector model.

Track 1: Adding like fractions: Example $\frac{1}{4} + \frac{1}{4} =$
Place the circle sector for $\frac{1}{4}$ in circle. Align one radius clockwise with the dashed starting line and the vertex with the center dot. Notice it covers $\frac{1}{4}$ of the circle and that the fraction is named in the outer ring. Place another $\frac{1}{4}$ adjacent to the $\frac{1}{4}$ in the circle. Notice that the union of the two parts covers the fraction named in the outer ring.

Track 2: Adding unlike fractions: Example $\frac{1}{4} + \frac{1}{2} =$
Place $\frac{1}{4}$ in the circle. Place $\frac{1}{2}$ adjacent to it. Read the outside ring.

Track 3: Subtracting fractions: Example $\frac{3}{4} - \frac{1}{2} =$
Cover the inner circle with $\frac{3}{4}$ aligning the sectors with the dashed starting line and center point moving clockwise. Cover $\frac{3}{4}$ with $\frac{1}{2}$ or remove $\frac{1}{2}$ and name the leftover or remaining fraction.

Common Denominators

FRACTION CDs

CD Play

Common Denominators

24

 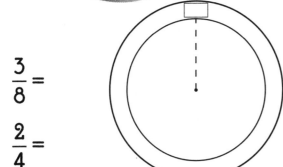

Try these addition/subtraction problems. Identify the CD and use colored pencils to show your work in color! Record equivalent fractions and the solution to the problem.

$$\frac{3}{8} =$$

$$+ \frac{2}{4} =$$ _____ _____

Color or shade in $\frac{3}{8}$ and $\frac{2}{4}$

$$\frac{2}{3} =$$

$$+ \frac{1}{4} =$$ _____ _____

Color or shade in $\frac{2}{3}$ and $\frac{1}{4}$

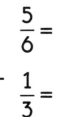 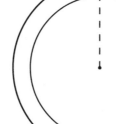

$$\frac{5}{6} =$$

$$- \frac{1}{3} =$$ _____ _____

Color or shade in $\frac{5}{6}$. Color over $\frac{1}{3}$ to show the difference.

$$\frac{1}{2} =$$

$$- \frac{2}{5} =$$ _____ _____

Color or shade in $\frac{1}{2}$. Color over $\frac{2}{5}$ to show the difference.

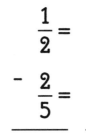 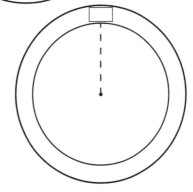

Counter-Point Calculator for fractions

Use your Collector CDs to solve these problems.

$$\begin{array}{r} \frac{1}{3} \\ + \frac{1}{8} \\ \hline \end{array}$$

$$\begin{array}{r} \frac{3}{16} \\ + \frac{3}{8} \\ \hline \end{array}$$

$$\begin{array}{r} \frac{3}{4} \\ + \frac{13}{16} \\ \hline \end{array}$$

$$\begin{array}{r} \frac{5}{6} \\ + \frac{7}{8} \\ \hline \end{array}$$

$$\begin{array}{r} \frac{2}{3} \\ + \frac{5}{8} \\ \hline \end{array}$$

$$\begin{array}{r} \frac{3}{16} \\ + \frac{5}{8} \\ \hline \end{array}$$

$$\begin{array}{r} \frac{7}{8} \\ - \frac{5}{12} \\ \hline \end{array}$$

$$\begin{array}{r} 1\frac{7}{8} \\ - \frac{5}{16} \\ \hline \end{array}$$

Make up your own problem:

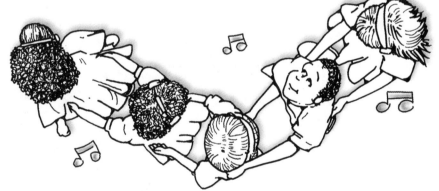

Think about your work. Explain how you figured out which CD to use.

SAMPLE CD
• A demo disc for finding common denominators

CD PLAY
• Common denominators

COLLECTOR'S CDs

Cut on the solid lines.
Fold on the dashed lines.
Glue flaps.

Topic
Fractions
   Decimal equivalents
   Percent equivalents

Learning Goals
- To represent and interpret fractions in a base-ten circle model
- To relate fractions, decimals, and percents
- To find equivalent representations

Guiding Document
NCTM Standards 2000*
- *Develop understanding of fractions as parts of unit wholes, as parts of a collection, as locations on number lines, and as divisions of whole numbers*
- *Use models, benchmarks, and equivalent forms to judge the size of fractions*
- *Recognize and generate equivalent forms of commonly used fractions, decimals, and percents*
- *Use visual models, benchmarks, and equivalent forms to add and subtract commonly used fractions and decimals*
- *Compare and order fractions, decimals, and percents efficiently and find their approximate locations on a number line*

Materials
For each small group of students:
   one set of AIMS Fraction Circle Model

For each student:
   a set of *What's the Point* circles, one in each of two colors
   scissors

Background Information
   In this activity students explore a circle divided into 10 equal sectors. Each sector represents $\frac{1}{10}$ of the whole, which may be written in the traditional form with a numerator and a denominator. It is appropriate to demonstrate that there is an alternate decimal form of notation, .1 or point one. Each fractional part of the circle may be written in the traditional form with a numerator and a denominator or as a decimal equivalent. Since each sector is divided into tenths, parts of the circle may be expressed in tenths and in hundredths.
   Using the AIMS Fraction Circle Models, students may compare one or more identical pieces to a corresponding part of the decimal circle and find the

decimal and percent equivalents. The circle model is only accurate to the nearest hundredth. Students will notice that if they cover $\frac{7}{8}$ of the circle that 8 sectors or tenths and between 87 and 88 hundredths will be covered. A decision then needs to be made to round up or down to obtain the approximate decimal value at .87 or .88.

Management
1. Students may work in small groups to share materials and to find and discuss the decimal and percent equivalents for a variety of fractions.
2. It may be worthwhile to distribute large chart paper to each group of students and simply ask them to make an organized record of all the possible fractions and their equivalents. The on-going discussion as they work together to justify their answers is a wonderful teaching strategy.
3. The teacher will need to prepare ahead of time, a set of *What's the Point* circles for each student—one circle in one color of card stock and one circle in a contrasting color.

Procedure
1. Distribute card stock circles to students and have them cut out one of each color.
2. Ask them to share with each other observations about the circles.
3. In whole class discussion, encourage students to share their observations—especially regarding the number of sectors [10], their relative size [equal], and the meaning of the small marks within each sector [tenths of tenths].
4. Direct students to cut each circle along the dashed line, the radius, from the edge of the circle to its center. Then show students how to combine circles so that two parts of the circle can be shown in contrasting colors.

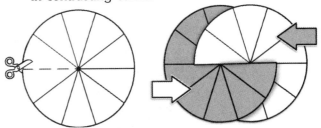

5. Spend some time exploring the overlapping circles to show various fractions and their "shadows" such as $\frac{3}{10}$ in one color and its complement $\frac{7}{10}$ in the other color.

6. Begin with tenths, the large sectors, and ask students how they could name the fraction in another way. [hundredths]
7. Ask students to find 25 hundredths. Pay particular attention to the idea that 25 hundredths is two tenths and five hundredths connecting it to a place value record of .2 and .05 or .25. Try other decimals such as .42, .67, .18, and so forth. Ask students to describe their answers in two ways.
8. Demonstrate to students that fractions with a denominator of 10 or 100 may also be written in decimal form because they are part of a base ten system that corresponds to our place value system. Thus two-tenths can be written in the traditional fraction form with a numerator of 2 and a denominator of 10 or in decimal form, .2.
9. Explain to students that they are going to use their fraction circle pieces and their *What's the Point* circles to explore decimal and percent equivalents. By placing one or more identical fraction circle parts on the *What's the Point* circle, students will translate the fraction to a decimal equivalent.
10. At this point, the teacher has the option of having students work together in small groups and organizing their discoveries on chart paper or having students work independently and using the table provided in the lesson.

Discussion
1. Describe the critical features of the *What's the Point* circles. [10 equal parts, each sector marked in ten equal parts]
2. How can the circle be used to convert a fraction to a decimal? [cover the circle with one or more identical plastic circle parts and interpret the part covered in tenths and/or hundredths]
3. How could simple addition and subtraction of decimals be completed with the overlapping circle model? For example, .3 plus .6 or .9 take away .4? [Slide the two circles parts together and uncover parts to add; cover to subtract.]

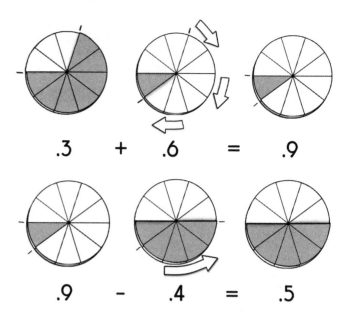

.3 + .6 = .9

.9 - .4 = .5

Evaluation
1. A simple, individual evaluation task: Given a set of five fractions a student will use the *What's the Point* model to show decimal and percent equivalents and be able to explain the process.
2. A more complex task: Give each student a card with one fraction, one decimal, and a percent, such as, $\frac{1}{5}$, .3, and 15%. [See *What's the Point* cards included]. Ask the student to discuss their relative sizes and to use pictures to support their explanations.

Evidence of Learning
1. Look for accurate translation of fraction to decimal to percent equivalent.
2. Look for illustration of relative size of fractions, decimals, and percent.
3. Listen for logical explanation of thinking that shows insight and understanding.

* Reprinted with permission from *Principles and Standards for School Mathematics*, 2000 by the National Council of Teachers of Mathematics. All rights reserved.

What's the Point?

What's the Point?

Use the circle model to find the decimal and percent equivalents for each fraction.

Fraction	Equivalent Base Ten Fraction	Decimal Equivalent		Percent Equivalent
		tenths	hundredths	
Example: $\frac{1}{2}$	$\frac{5}{10}$	.5	.50	50%
$\frac{2}{5}$				
$\frac{1}{4}$				
$\frac{4}{5}$				
$\frac{3}{4}$				
$\frac{2}{8}$				
$\frac{6}{8}$				
$\frac{1}{12}$				
$\frac{3}{8}$				

What's the Point?

Distribute one card to each student or pair of students or small group. Have students illustrate and explain, in pictures and words, the relationships and relative size of the numbers on each card.

$\frac{1}{5}$	.3	15%	$\frac{1}{2}$	.49	55%
$\frac{1}{3}$	.4	25%	$\frac{3}{8}$	.3	40%
$\frac{5}{6}$	.9	80%	$\frac{2}{3}$	.7	58%
$\frac{2}{5}$	.6	35%	$\frac{3}{4}$	.8	70%
$\frac{1}{4}$	.4	30%	$\frac{1}{6}$	.2	12%
$\frac{5}{8}$	.8	65%	$\frac{5}{12}$	.5	38%
$\frac{7}{12}$	.55	60%	$\frac{4}{5}$	.75	92%

Topic
Decimals as base ten fractions
  Comparing
  Ordering
  Place value concepts: tenths, hundredths, thousandths

Learning Goals
- To understand relative magnitude of decimals
- To practice ordering decimals
- To experience coins (dimes and cents) as a model for understanding decimals as base-ten fractions

Guiding Document
NCTM Standard 2000*
- *Compare and order fractions, decimals, and percents efficiently and find their approximate locations on a number line*

Materials
For each team of four students:
  one length of string or "fat" yarn (24"-30")
  set of 7 pieces of "folding money" made from 5" x 8" index cards
  a brown paper lunch bag to serve as the "money bag"

For two-place money:
  Set A and D: .25 .2   .03 .47 .3   .4   .36
  Set B and E: .1   .01 .11 .14 .2   .28 .06
  Set C and F: .52 .21 .09 .17 .1   .49 .5

For three-place money:
  Set A and D:.173 .24   .039 .107 .17 .201 .18
  Set B and E: .6   .073 .48 .602 .61 .12 .3
  Set C and F: .508 .468 .51 .49 .511 .509 .47

Background Information
Students frequently have difficulty ordering decimal numbers in an ascending or descending sequence. In order to master such a skill, practice, reinforcement and repetition are necessary in a setting that maintains their interest. In this activity students connect their prior experience with dimes and cents to tenths and hundredths respectively. The lesson provides playful, intelligent practice in a cooperative team setting.

Each team of four students is given a set of 5-7 pieces of "folding money" marked in decimal units and instructed to hang it on the clothesline in ascending or descending order.

Management
1. Prior to the lesson, prepare six sets of folding money by copying the three decimal sets provided onto folded index cards such that the value can be read on either side of the fold.

2. Each set is produced twice so that teams with matching sets can trade places and audit each other's work. (See *Materials.* For example, Sets A and D are the same.) Use a different color index card for each pair of money sets.

Procedure
1. Tell the students that they are going to use what they know about dimes and cents to put a set of decimal numbers in order from smallest to largest.
2. Discuss the relative values of dimes and cents. (Trade is ten cents for one dime.)
3. Set the stage by describing this make-believe setting.
   In the country of No-Centsability moneymakers produce only folding money equivalent to dimes and cents in our world. They are eager to make a point in their accounting system so they record the value of their money like this: .5 (read point or dot five) means five dimes and .03 (point or dot zero three) means 3 cents or 3 pennies. Any combination of numbers after the point corresponds to our dimes and pennies. Furthermore, they have an additional coin called non-cents which is one tenth of a cent and is represented in our decimal system by thousandths. Thus in the land of No-Centsability .325 would mean 3 dimes, 2 cents and 5 non-cents.
4. Ask students if they understand. Instruct them to turn to their neighbor and explain what .03 means [3 cents], what .6 means [6 dimes], what .24 means [2 dimes and 4 cents], and what .235 means [2 dimes, 3 cents and 5 non-cents].
5. Tell the students they will be working in teams to hang their new folding money on a clothesline in ascending order from left to right.

6. Distribute a set of folding money in a money bag and a clothesline to each team. Each pair of teams will receive identical sets of money.

7. At a designated time have teams begin sequencing their decimals. Direct two students to hold up the ends of the line and the other two to put the money in order.

8. Have the two teams with identical sets of decimals audit each other's work. Invite them to meet and discuss how their work is similar or dissimilar and to discuss their reasoning.

9. An alternative is to have teams compete against each other for speed and accuracy.

Discussion

1. How are dimes and pennies related? [10 pennies make a dime]

2. How are non-cents related to cents or pennies? [10 non-cents make a cent or penny]

3. How are dimes, cents, and non-cents related to a dollar? [one tenth, one hundredth, and one-thousandth respectively]

4. How could these values be written as fractions with a numerator and a denominator? [$\frac{1}{10}, \frac{1}{100}, \frac{1}{1000}$]

5. What do you think happens to the denominator when we write these values as decimal numbers? [The denominator becomes a value by position or place in our base ten system.]

6. How is it helpful to relate putting in order a series of decimal numbers to what we know about our own money system?

7. How can you explain which decimal is larger: .6 or .621? [.621 is larger because you have 1 non-cent and 2 cents more than 6 dimes]

Evaluation

For individual evaluation distribute *Show Me the Money* where students independently order several sets of decimals.

Evidence of Learning

1. Look for accuracy in the ordering of decimals.

2. Listen for evidence of understanding in students' explanations of their reasoning.

3. Watch for interaction between students in informal discussion. Listen for comments like, "I don't get it" or "I think this is right because ...."

4. In conversation with students, ask if they can create or invent an example of their own that shows they understand.

* Reprinted with permission from *Principles and Standards for School Mathematics,* 2000 by the National Council of Teachers of Mathematics. All rights reserved.

Show Me the Money

Hang these decimals on the line in order from least to most.

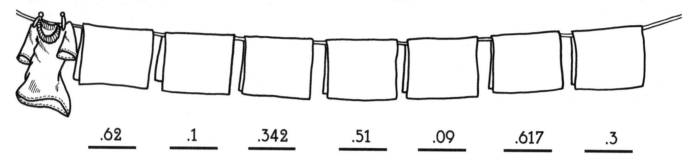

.62   .1   .342   .51   .09   .617   .3

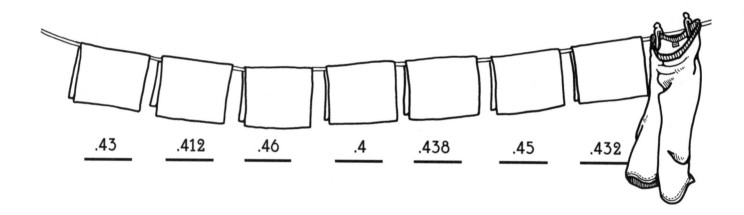

.43   .412   .46   .4   .438   .45   .432

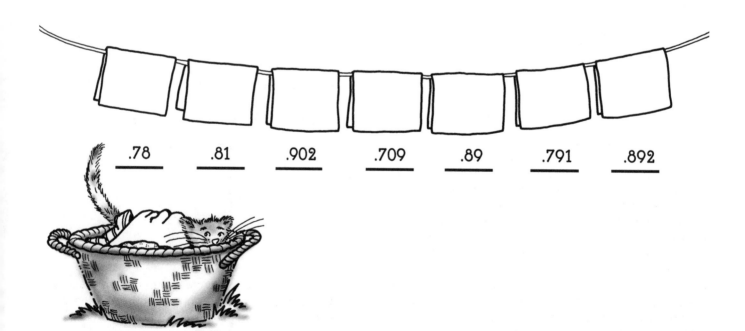

.78   .81   .902   .709   .89   .791   .892

Fraction on the Fringe Cutting Edge

Topic
Fractions: length model
  fair shares
  equivalency

Learning Goals
- To understand relative size of fractions by direct comparison using a linear model
- To recognize and name fractions as fair shares of a linear unit
- To construct a linear model that represents equivalent fractions and proportionality

Guiding Document
NCTM Standards 2000*
- *Develop understanding of fractions as parts of unit wholes, as parts of a collection, as locations on number lines, and as divisions of whole numbers*
- *Use models, benchmarks, and equivalent forms to judge the size of fractions*
- *Recognize and generate equivalent forms of commonly used fractions, decimals, and percents*
- *Compare and order fractions, decimals, and percents efficiently and find their approximate locations on a number line*

Materials
Duplicating paper ($8 \frac{1}{2}$ x 11 inches) in 7 bright colors, cut into $4 \frac{1}{4}$ x 11 inch pieces
Black construction paper, 12 x 18 inches, cut into $4 \frac{1}{4}$ x 6 inch pieces
Scissors
Staplers
Rulers

Background Information
A useful model for exploring equivalency is based on a line or bar that represents the whole. In this activity a set of colored papers that shares a common linear measure becomes a tool for comparing relative sizes of fractions and also for recognizing and naming equivalent fractions.

When students use this model to find the missing number in two equivalent fractions (see *Fringe Benefits*), they have the opportunity to discover some number patterns and relationships. These include: numerator is to numerator in the same relationship as denominator is to denominator; numerator and denominator of one fraction are in the same relationship as numerator and denominator of second fraction; and cross products are equal.

Procedure
1. Distribute seven lengths of brightly colored paper and four pieces of black paper to each pair of students.
2. Have students separate colors into two sets: one of three colors and the other of four colors.
3. Tell them to begin with the four color stack. Direct them to stack four colors on top of one another and bend into a curve so that the ends of the layers of color are off-set by about $\frac{1}{2}$ inch at each end.

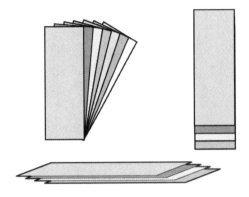

4. Tell them to hold papers in position and fold entire set in half and cut along fold line.

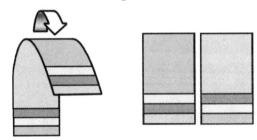

5. Now there are two sets of four colors—one set per student.
6. Have each student place a piece of black paper beneath the colored stack in such a way that a $\frac{1}{2}$ inch black border is formed at the layered end. Staple in two places at the opposite end.

7. Tell them to turn or rotate the stapled stack so that black is on the bottom and the stapled part is at the top. The black band represents the whole number ONE and is never cut.

8. Tell them to use scissors to cut all colored layers (not the black) in half vertically to about the middle of the top sheet.

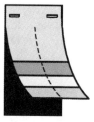

9. Have students cut ONLY second, third, and fourth colored layers in half again. Check to make sure top three layers are now cut into four equal pieces.

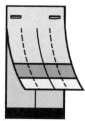

10. Have students cut ONLY third and fourth layers in half again thus resulting in eight equal pieces in each layer.

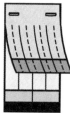

11. Have students cut ONLY the top layer (fourth layer) in half again resulting in sixteen equal pieces.

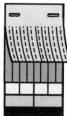

12. Inform the students that they are going to repeat the entire procedure with the set of three colors and cutting in thirds, then in half (for sixths), and finally in half again to produce twelfths.

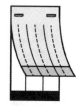

13. Have students use the model to complete the proportional reasoning problems in *Fringe Benefits*. Notice that one page is designed for use with each model and one is for mixed use.

Discussion

1. What part of the layered paper model is uniform or the same for all layers? [the $4\frac{1}{4}$ inch edge]
2. How are the layers different? [Each layer has more parts and the parts are smaller.]
3. How could you explain the relationship of one layer to its immediate neighbor above or below it? [The pieces are half the size if the layer is above it and double the size if the layer is beneath it.]
4. What is the relationship of the numerator and the denominator to this model? [The numerator describes the number of parts under consideration and the denominator tells the size of the parts or the number of parts in the whole.]
5. What number patterns or relationships did you discover when using your fraction fringe to complete *Fringe Benefits*? (See *Background Information*. Students may notice that one numerator is twice the size of the other numerator and that the denominators are likewise. Answers will vary.)
6. How could you solve a similar problem which is not represented by the paper model? For instance, $\frac{4}{12} = \frac{?}{24}$. [If the relationship is understood, it could be applied to any problem. Since 12 is half of 24, then 4 must be half of the missing number, 8. Or since 4 is $\frac{1}{3}$ of 12, then the missing number must be $\frac{1}{3}$ of 24, or 8. Or the cross products are equal and 4 times 24 is 96, therefore something (8) times 12 is 96.]
7. Explain how one of the models could illustrate units of liquid measure beginning with one gallon. [gallon, half gallon, quart, pints, cups]

Evaluation

Since three pages of *Fraction Fringe* are included with this lesson, any of the sets could be used as an independent evaluation of understanding.

Evidence of Learning

1. Look for accuracy of missing numbers in ratios.
2. Listen for intelligent questions. Thinkers ask good questions that demand thoughtful answers beyond yes or no. Acknowledge good questions from students.
3. Listen for insight about relationships among numbers that shows connections to past learning or to new ideas. For instance, recognizing a relationship already learned in a multiplication table of whole numbers and now applied to numerators or denominators of fractions is a good example of connecting to prior learning in a new setting.
4. Look for pictures that match accurately the ratio and proportion.
5. Watch faces for expressions of frustration or satisfaction.

* Reprinted with permission from *Principles and Standards for School Mathematics,* 2000 by the National Council of Teachers of Mathematics. All rights reserved.

Use the four-layer model of fraction fringe to fill in the missing numbers. Record your answer in the empty square.

$$\frac{1}{2} = \frac{\boxed{}}{4} \qquad \frac{4}{8} = \frac{1}{\boxed{}} \qquad \frac{1}{\boxed{}} = \frac{4}{16} \qquad \frac{\boxed{}}{8} = \frac{10}{16} \qquad \frac{\boxed{}}{4} = \frac{6}{8}$$

$$\frac{3}{8} = \frac{\boxed{}}{16} \qquad \frac{7}{\boxed{}} = \frac{14}{16} \qquad \frac{8}{\boxed{}} = \frac{2}{4} \qquad \frac{6}{8} = \frac{\boxed{}}{16}$$

1. Find and describe some number patterns you observed in the relationships above.

2. Choose one ratio and proportion and draw a picture that shows how the two fractions are equivalent.

3. How could these number patterns be helpful to you?

Use the three-layer model of fraction fringe to fill in the missing numbers. Record your answer in the empty square.

$$\frac{2}{3} = \frac{\square}{6}$$

$$\frac{5}{6} = \frac{10}{\square}$$

$$\frac{1}{3} = \frac{2}{\square}$$

$$\frac{1}{6} = \frac{\square}{12}$$

$$\frac{4}{6} = \frac{2}{\square}$$

$$\frac{4}{\square} = \frac{1}{3}$$

$$\frac{4}{\square} = \frac{8}{12}$$

$$\frac{5}{\square} = \frac{10}{12}$$

$$\frac{8}{12} = \frac{\square}{3}$$

1. Find and describe some number patterns you observed in the relationships above.

2. Choose one ratio and proportion and draw a picture that shows how the two fractions are equivalent.

3. How could a pattern help you figure out $\dfrac{2}{\square} = \dfrac{1}{12}$?

Use both fraction fringe models to find the missing parts. Record your answers in the empty squares.

$$\frac{2}{3} = \frac{\boxed{}}{6}$$

$$\frac{4}{8} = \frac{1}{\boxed{}}$$

$$\frac{\boxed{}}{4} = \frac{6}{8}$$

$$\frac{1}{3} = \frac{2}{\boxed{}}$$

$$\frac{3}{8} = \frac{\boxed{}}{16}$$

$$\frac{4}{6} = \frac{2}{\boxed{}}$$

$$\frac{6}{8} = \frac{\boxed{}}{16}$$

$$\frac{4}{\boxed{}} = \frac{1}{3}$$

$$\frac{4}{\boxed{}} = \frac{8}{12}$$

$$\frac{\boxed{}}{8} = \frac{10}{16}$$

$$\frac{8}{\boxed{}} = \frac{2}{4}$$

$$\frac{7}{\boxed{}} = \frac{14}{16}$$

	1	2	3	4	5	6	7	8	9	10	11	12
1	1	2	3	4	5	6	7	8	9	10	11	12
2	2	4	6	8	10	12	14	16	18	20	22	24
3	3	6	9	12	15	18	21	24	27	30	33	36
4	4	8	12	16	20	24	28	32	36	40	44	48
5	5	10	15	20	25	30	35	40	45	50	55	60
6	6	12	18	24	30	36	42	48	54	60	66	72
7	7	14	21	28	35	42	49	56	63	70	77	84
8									80	88	96	
9									90	99	108	
									100	110	120	
									110	121	132	
	24	36				84	96	108	120	132	144	

Describe how these proportions can be found in a multiplication table of whole numbers.

Multiplication Table

	1	2	3	4	5	6	7	8	9
1	1	2	3	4	5	6	7	8	9
2	2	4	6	8	10	12	14	16	18
3	3	6	9	12	15	18	21	24	27
4	4	8	12	16	20	24	28	32	36
5	5	10	15	20	25	30	35	40	45
6	6	12	18	24	30	36	42	48	54
7	7	14	21	28	35	42	49	56	63
8	8	16	24	32	40	48	56	64	72
9	9	18	27	36	45	54	63	72	81

Name

Topic
Fractions
  Equivalency

Learning Goals
- To construct a model for generating equivalent fractions
- To promote meaning in building a table of fraction equivalents connected to the multiplication table and multiple names for ONE

Guiding Document
NCTM Standard 2000*
- *Recognize and generate equivalent forms of commonly used fractions, decimals, and percents*

Materials
Per student:
  10 wide craft sticks
  fine line marking pen
  multiplication table
  2 six-inch strips masking tape

Background Information
Equivalent fractions may be generated symbolically by multiplying the numerator and the denominator of a fraction by the same number. This action is the same as multiplying the fraction by another name for ONE where the numerator and denominator are the same, e.g., $\frac{2}{2}$, $\frac{3}{3}$, $\frac{4}{4}$, etc. The number ONE is the *identity element* for multiplication. Any number multiplied by ONE remains the same. This is known as the identity property of rational numbers. Thus $\frac{3}{4} = \frac{3}{4} \times 1 = \frac{3}{4} \times \frac{2}{2}$ $= \frac{6}{8}$. Any fraction of the form $\frac{n}{n}$ can be used as the identity element.

While students may memorize this rule, building a frame of reference connected to the multiplication table provides an opportunity to discuss how each equivalent fraction is a result of such a multiplication operation. Each column in the table is headed by a number that represents a name for ONE where the numerator and denominator have been multiplied by that number.

Procedure
1. Distribute the multiplication table and encourage a discussion of patterns and relationships. Try to get students to recognize that the numbers in each row or column skip count by the number that heads each column or row.
2. Distribute marking pens, sticks, and masking tape to each small working group of students.
3. Explain that each student will need ten sticks. Have students line up all 10 sticks parallel to each other and close but not touching.

4. Show students how to carefully tape sticks to form a "raft" with small spaces between each stick. The taped side will be the back side.

5. Instruct them to turn the raft over and label the sticks in such a way that the top row names the counting numbers from 1-10; the second row skip counts by two from 2-20; the third row skip counts by three from 3-30 and so forth. Continue skip counting for each stick through tens.

6. Instruct students to select two neighboring rows and consider one as the numerator and the other as the denominator of a series of fractions.

7. Tell students to be prepared to describe any patterns or observations made about their name frames. [Equivalent fractions line up when one stick is the numerator and the other is the denominator.]

Discussion

1. How are the numbers on each row related to the first or head number on that stick? [Numbers are skip counted by that number.]

2. How are the numbers in each column related to the top or first number in each column? [Numbers are skip counted according to the leading number in the column.]

3. Explain to your neighbor how you could use the "name frame" to find $\frac{12}{16}$ in lowest terms. [Find $\frac{12}{16}$ and move to the left-most column and read the fraction in the corresponding rows.]

4. Explain to your neighbor how you could find an equivalent for $\frac{1}{2}$ in highest terms. [Find $\frac{1}{2}$ and move to the furthest position to the right.]

5. What patterns can you find in this table of equivalents? [Cross-products of equivalent fractions are equal.]

6. Explain how to name an equivalent fraction, including those not on the "chart." [Multiply the fraction by another name for ONE. Multiply the numerator and the denominator by the same number.]

Evaluation

Ask students, individually or as a group to find three equivalent fractions for a given fraction such as $\frac{1}{2}$.

Have them draw a picture that shows how these fractions are the same size and why their names are different. Encourage them to use their prior experience with familiar models such as the circle model, length model, or unit square model.

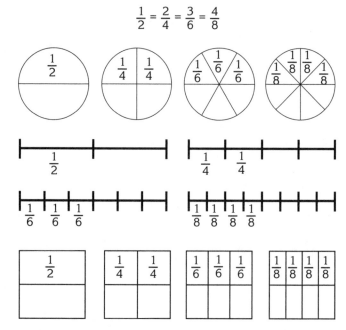

Have them explain why the value or size of an equivalent fraction remains the same even though the numbers are different.

Evidence of Learning

1. Look for accurate equivalents for the fraction.

2. Look for pictures that illustrate correctly three equivalent fractions.

3. Listen for explanations of thinking that show understanding and insight.

* Reprinted with permission from *Principles and Standards for School Mathematics*, 2000 by the National Council of Teachers of Mathematics. All rights reserved.

1	2	3	4	5	6	7	8	9	10
2	4	6	8	10	12	14	16	18	20
3	6	9	12	15	18	21	24	27	30
4	8	12	16	20	24	28	32	36	40
5	10	15	20	25	30	35	40	45	50
6	12	18	24	30	36	42	48	54	60
7	14	21	28	35	42	49	56	63	70
8	16	24	32	40	48	56	64	72	80
9	18	27	36	45	54	63	72	81	90
10	20	30	40	50	60	70	80	90	100

SLIDE RULER FRACTIONS

Topic
Fractions

Parallel number lines with unit fractions and their multiples

Understanding relative size of fractions on a number line

Learning Goals
- To order fractions on a number line, such as a ruler
- To experience addition and subtraction of fractions on a number line
- To connect fractions and linear measurement

Guiding Document
NCTM Standards 2000*
- *Develop understanding of fractions as parts of unit wholes, as parts of collections, as locations on number lines, and as division of whole numbers*
- *Use visual models, benchmarks, and equivalent forms to add and subtract commonly used fractions and decimals*
- *Compare and order fractions, decimals, and percents efficiently and find their approximate locations on a number line*

Materials
Colored paper strips
Scissors
Standard ruler
Centimeter ruler

Background Information
The model for exploring fractions in this lesson is a measured model where lengths are compared. Lines are drawn and subdivided or physical models such as paper strips are compared on the basis of length. A corresponding application is made with decimal strips.

Connections can be made to linear measure: fractions to inches and fractional parts; decimals to metric measures.

Management
1. Prior to the lesson, cut colored paper into lengths of 4" x 1". Each student will need four strips.
2. Duplicate one *Slide Ruler B* for each student. Also duplicate one *Decimal Ruler B* for each student.

3. It may be beneficial to make transparencies of the *Slide Ruler* and *Decimal Ruler* so that the process of addition and subtraction may be demonstrated to the students.

Procedure
Construction of paper fraction strips (Folding Fractions)
1. Distribute four lengths (4" x 1") of colored paper to each student. Guide the folding and recording of each fraction fold and corresponding number line according to the instructions on the activity page: *Folding Fractions.*

Application of Slide Rulers
1. Distribute one *Slide Ruler B* to each student. Ask them how the *Slide Ruler* is like the paper strips they just folded. Inform them that they will now use the *Slide Rulers* to add and subtract fractions.
2. Take the students through the instructions to *Slide Ruler Fractions.*

To add two fractions, such as $\frac{5}{8} + \frac{3}{16}$, find the first fraction, $\frac{5}{8}$, on Ruler A. Then align 0 on Ruler B with $\frac{5}{8}$ mark on Ruler A. Then slide (your finger) to the right along Ruler B to the mark of the second fraction, $\frac{3}{16}$. Read the answer ($\frac{13}{16}$) directly above on Ruler A.

To subtract two fractions, such as $\frac{7}{8} - \frac{3}{4}$. Align 0 of Ruler B with the minuend, the larger number ($\frac{7}{8}$) on Ruler A. Find the subtrahend ($\frac{3}{4}$) on Ruler B and slide it to the left until $\frac{3}{4}$ on Ruler B is aligned with $\frac{7}{8}$ on A. Read the difference on Ruler A directly above the 0 on Ruler B.

Discussion
1. What fractions are represented on the *Slide Ruler*? [halves, fourths, eighths, sixteenths]
2. How does folding strips of paper help you understand the meaning of half, fourth, and eighth? [Folding a strip of paper into two equal parts models dividing a line segment in half. Similarly, folding into four equal parts models fourths, and eight equal parts models eighths.]
3. When partitioning a line segment into equal parts such as halves, fourths, eighths and sixteenths, how could these parts be distinguished if they cannot be labeled symbolically? [The lines that partition the line segment could be of different lengths. (Notice on a standard ruler that the mark for one half is longer than the marks for fourths, etc.)]

4. Explain how a move or slide to the right models the addition process. [When lengths are added they are placed end to end thus increasing the total measure.]
5. Explain how a move or slide to the left is a model for subtraction. [Moving or sliding to the left models covering part of the length and naming what is leftover. Another model is simply comparing the two lengths by matching one set of end points.

Procedure

Application for Decimals Rule, Too
1. Distribute a *Decimal Ruler B* to each student.
2. Take the students through the instructions to *Decimal Slide Rules.*

   To add two decimals, such as .7 + .45, find the first decimal, .7, on Ruler A. Then align 0 on Ruler B with .7 mark on Ruler A. Then slide your finger to the right along Ruler B to the mark of the second decimal, .45. Read the answer (1.15) directly above on Ruler A.

   To subtract two decimals, such as 1.2 – .75, align 0 of Ruler B with the minuend, the larger number (1.2) on Ruler A. Find the subtrahend (.75) on Slide Ruler B and slide it to the left the length of the subtrahend matching .75 on Ruler B with 1.2 on Ruler A. Read the difference (.45) on Ruler A directly above the 0 on Ruler B.

Discussion
1. What decimals are represented on the Slide Ruler? [tenths and hundredths]
2. How are these decimal numbers related to a metric ruler?[Tenths represent centimeters and hundredths represent millimeters.]

Evaluation
1. Using two standard rulers, have students apply the slide ruler technique to add these lengths.

$$\frac{3}{4} + \frac{2}{8} + \frac{5}{16}$$

Ask them to explain how they solved the problem. Direct the students to make up a problem for your partner to try. Have students explain their thinking.

Evidence of Learning
1. Look to see if students are able to apply or transfer their understanding of fraction slide rulers to standard rulers and linear measurement.

FOLDING FRACTIONS

Fold each strip as directed. Label each fraction part.
Attach the paper strip directly above the number line. Label the fractions on the number line between 0 and 1.

Fold once.
Record the fraction parts.
Label the number line.

0 ———————————————————— 1

Fold twice.
Record previous fractions first.
Record the new fraction parts.
Label the number line.

0 ———————————————————— 1

Fold three times.
Record previous fractions first.
Record the new fraction parts.
Label the number line.

0 ———————————————————— 1

Fold four times.
Record the previous fractions first.
Record new fraction parts.

0 ———————————————————— 1

SLIDE RULER FRACTIONS

Try these problems and record your answers.

Fraction Slide Rules:

1. Cut out Slide Ruler B.

2. **To add** two fractions, such as $\frac{5}{8} + \frac{3}{16}$, find the first fraction, $\frac{5}{8}$, on Ruler A. Then align 0 on Ruler B with $\frac{5}{8}$ mark on Ruler A. Then slide your finger to the right along Ruler B to the mark of the second fraction, $\frac{3}{16}$. Read the answer ($\frac{3}{16}$) directly above on Ruler A.

3. To **subtract** two fractions, such as $\frac{7}{8} - \frac{3}{4}$. Align 0 of Ruler B with the minuend, the larger number ($\frac{7}{8}$) on Ruler A. Find the subtrahend on Slide Ruler B and slide it to the left until $\frac{3}{4}$ on Ruler B is aligned with $\frac{7}{8}$ on A. Read the difference on Ruler A directly above the 0 on Ruler B.

Add: (Slide to the right!)

$$\frac{7}{16} + \frac{3}{4} \qquad \frac{5}{8} + \frac{11}{16} \qquad \frac{3}{4} + \frac{5}{16} \qquad \frac{13}{16} + \frac{3}{8}$$

Subtract: (Slide to the left!)

$$\frac{15}{16} - \frac{1}{4} \qquad \frac{5}{8} - \frac{3}{16} \qquad \frac{7}{8} - \frac{3}{4} \qquad \frac{3}{8} - \frac{3}{16}$$

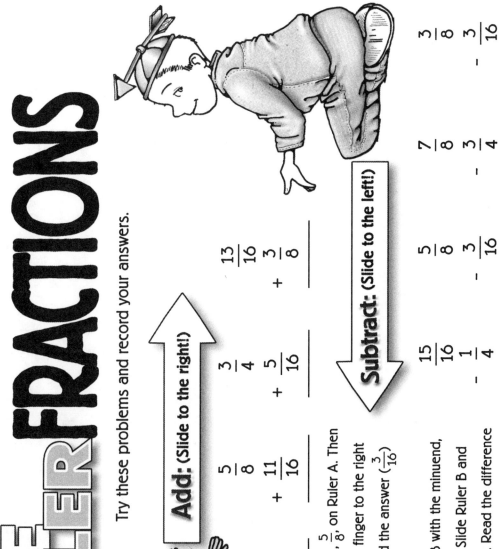

Slide Ruler A

SLIDE RULER FRACTIONS

Slide Ruler B

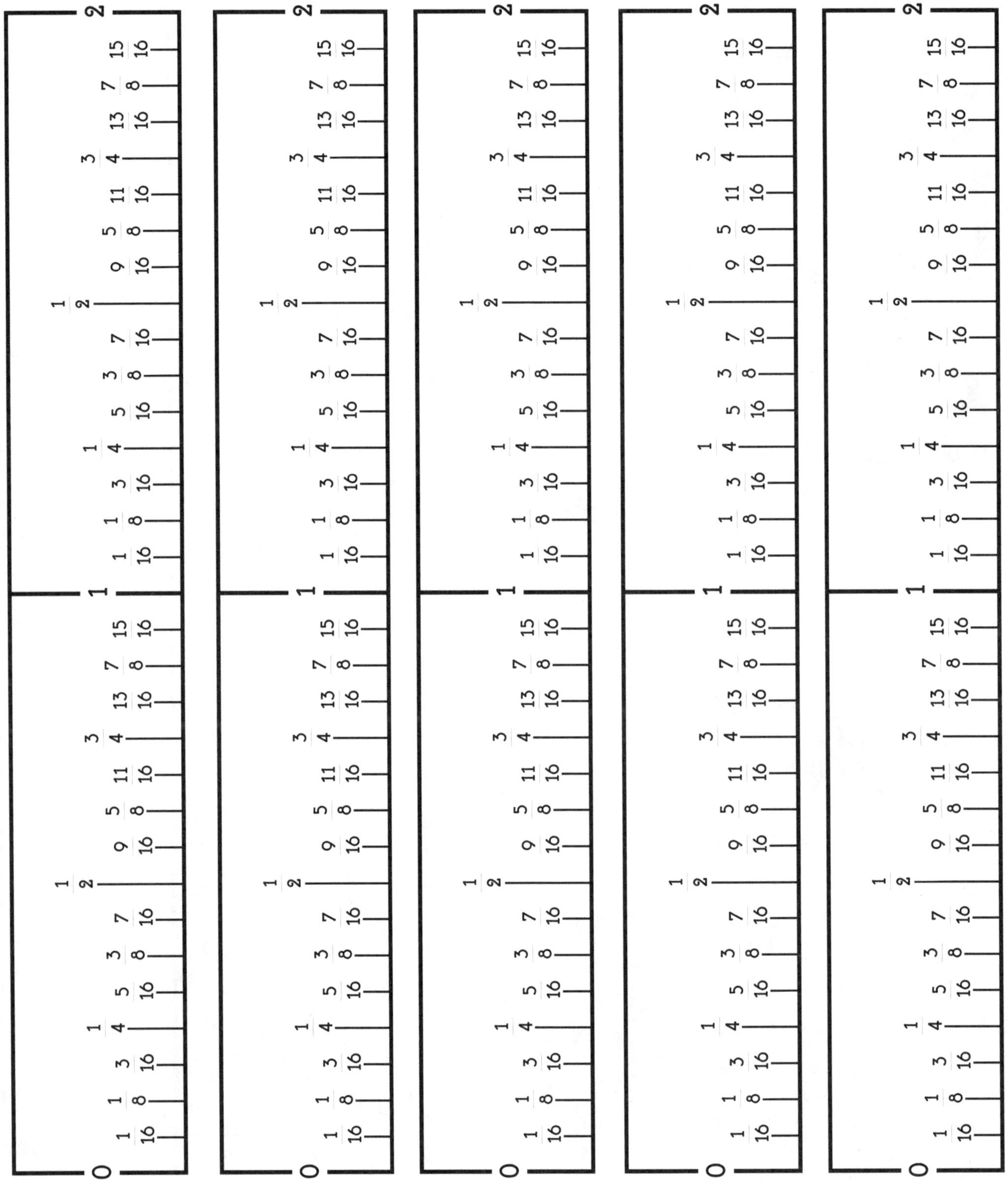

DECIMALS RULE, TOO

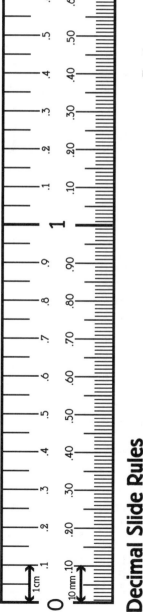

Decimal Ruler A

Try these problems and record your answers.

Decimal Slide Rules

1. Cut out Decimal Slide Ruler B for decimals.

2. To add two decimals, such as .7 + .45, find the first decimal, .7, on Ruler A. Then align 0 on Ruler B with .7 mark on Ruler A. Then slide your finger to the right along Ruler B to the mark of the second decimal, .45. Read the answer (1.15) directly above on Ruler A.

3. To subtract two decimals, such as 1.2 – .75, align 0 of Ruler B with the minuend, the larger number (1.2) on Ruler A. Find the subtrahend (.75) on Slide Ruler B and slide it to the left the length of the subtrahend matching .75 on Ruler B with 1.2 on Ruler A. Read the difference (.45) on Ruler A directly above the 0 on Ruler B.

Add: (Slide to the right!)

$$\begin{array}{r} .7 \\ + .55 \\ \hline \end{array} \qquad \begin{array}{r} 1.19 \\ + .64 \\ \hline \end{array} \qquad \begin{array}{r} 1.2 \\ + .34 \\ \hline \end{array}$$

$$\begin{array}{r} .4 \\ + .85 \\ \hline \end{array}$$

Subtract: (Slide to the left!)

$$\begin{array}{r} 1.9 \\ - .5 \\ \hline \end{array} \qquad \begin{array}{r} .87 \\ - .15 \\ \hline \end{array} \qquad \begin{array}{r} 1.25 \\ - .75 \\ \hline \end{array} \qquad \begin{array}{r} 1.73 \\ - .95 \\ \hline \end{array}$$

51

DECIMALS RULE, TOO

Decimal Ruler B

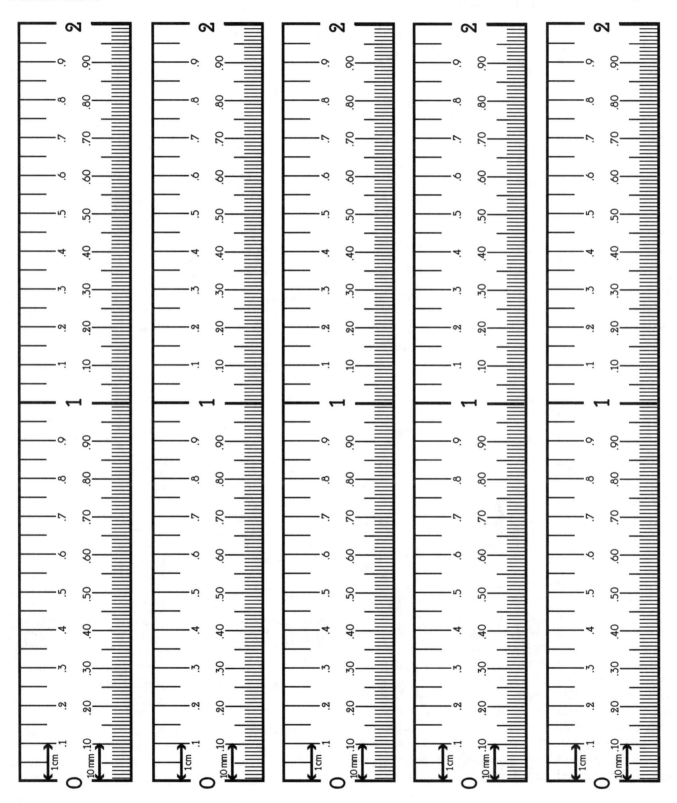

52 © 2004 AIMS Education Foundation

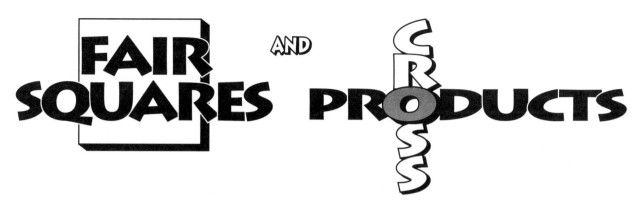

Topic
Fractions

Unit squares as an area model for multiplication

Learning Goals
- To promote understanding of multiplication of fractions using an area model
- To connect understanding of multiplication of whole numbers to that of fractions
- To provide a way to picture the meaning of multiplication
- To clarify meaning of numerator and denominator

Guiding Document
NCTM Standards 2000*
- *Develop understanding of fractions as parts of unit wholes, as parts of a collection, as locations on number lines, and as divisions of whole numbers*
- *Use models, benchmarks, and equivalent forms to judge the size of fractions*
- *Understand the meaning and effects of arithmetic operations with fractions, decimals, and integers*
- *Develop and analyze algorithms for computing with fractions, decimals, and integers and develop fluency in their use*

Materials
For each group of two students:
set of AIMS Fractional Transparencies
colored pencils
rulers (optional)

Background Information
In order to facilitate understanding of the meaning of the operation of multiplication of fractions, it is necessary and useful that we reflect on our understanding of multiplication of whole numbers.

One practical model is an area model where two measures, represented by whole numbers 3 and 4, for example, are the length and width of a rectangular region. To determine the area, we fill in perpendicular lines to form square units as pictured and determine the total area. The first frame shows 3 parts and the second frame shows 4 parts. When both frames are superimposed and perpendicular, their cross

product shows 12 square units. The squares must be congruent, thus fair squares, and when they are "crossed" they form cross products.

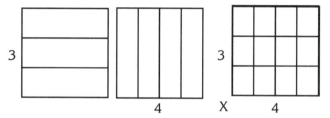

This explanation makes sense for students when considering multiplication of whole numbers. It is remarkably helpful when used with fractions too. Using the same model, the unit square is marked or divided into fair shares representing the denominator of a fraction and the numerator of the fraction under consideration is shaded or tinted. Then the units squares representing the two fractions to be multiplied are superimposed in a perpendicular manner showing the cross product. Students can then see how the product is formed and why multiplication of whole numbers produces a larger number while multiplication of fractions produces a smaller number. For example, $\frac{1}{3}$ of $\frac{2}{4}$ or $\frac{1}{3}$ x $\frac{2}{4}$ could be pictured as shown. One third of one unit is shaded and $\frac{2}{4}$ of another unit square is shaded. The two are then placed perpendicular forming 12 equal shares—the denominator of the product, and the number of shares shaded by both squares, 2, is the numerator of the cross product.

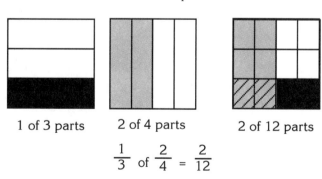

| 1 of 3 parts | 2 of 4 parts | 2 of 12 parts |

$$\frac{1}{3} \text{ of } \frac{2}{4} = \frac{2}{12}$$

Management
1. Students need to share materials in this activity. There are many ways to be creative in the sharing of materials. Working in pairs is ideal since there

are double sets of fractions in the AIMS Fractional Transparencies, one in each of two colors.

2. If there are not enough sets of AIMS Fractional Transparencies, duplicate the fractions squares included with this lesson on transparency film.

Procedure

1. Distribute to each group of 3-4 students a set of AIMS Fractional Transparencies, colored pencils and one activity sheet per person: *Fair Squares and Cross Products.*

2. Tell students that they will be using the square models in the empty frame to solve the problem. Explain that they will be making a picture record of each factor and then the corresponding product.

Discussion

1. Why are these squares called fair squares? [Their size and shape are identical.]

2. Why do we get a larger number when we multiply whole numbers and a smaller number when we multiply fractions? [When we multiply whole numbers, we are combining complete sets, and when we multiply fractions, we are combining parts of partial sets.]

3. How does the multiplication table for whole numbers relate to understanding multiplication of fractions? [The numerators increase by multiples found in the multiplication table as do the denominators.]

Evaluation

1. Several levels of evaluation are available. At one level, students use the model to solve some problems by selecting the matching fraction squares and cross products.

2. At another level, students draw the factors in separate squares and determine the answer.

3. At still another level, students use the model to solve the problem and illustrate their work in one square with two different colors to show the cross product. See activity pages *Cross Products.*

Evidence of Learning

1. Look for pictures that accurately match the fractions and that the factors are placed perpendicular to each other.

2. Listen to students' explanations of their illustrations of the problem and the product.

* Reprinted with permission from *Principles and Standards for School Mathematics,* 2000 by the National Council of Teachers of Mathematics. All rights reserved.

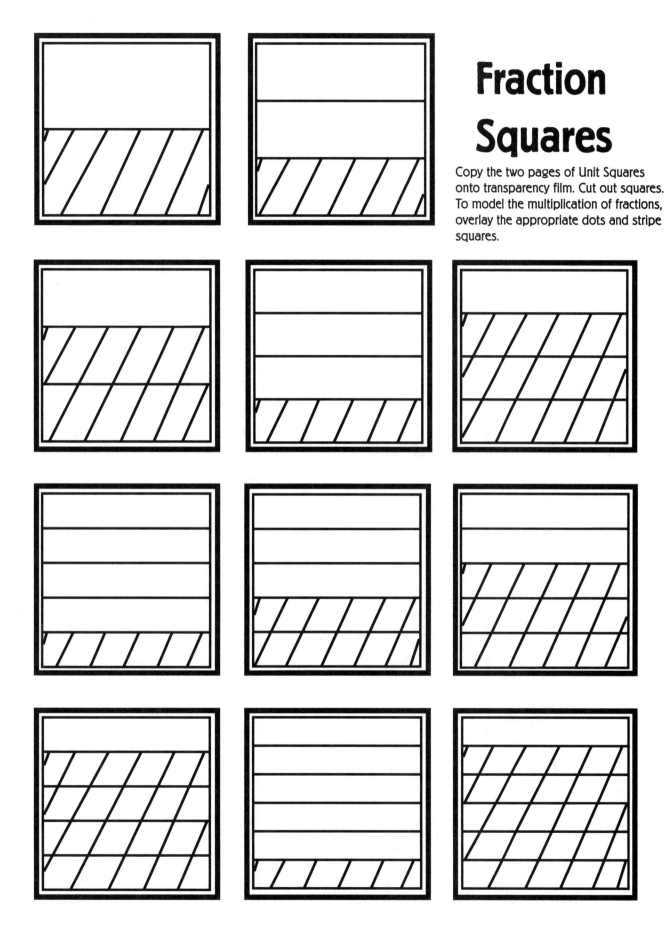

Fraction

Squares

Copy the two pages of Unit Squares onto transparency film. Cut out squares. To model the multiplication of fractions, overlay the appropriate dots and stripe squares.

Fraction
Squares

Copy the two pages of Unit Squares onto transparency film. Cut out squares. To model the multiplication of fractions, overlay the appropriate dots and stripe squares.

AND

PRODUCTS

Use the model.
Make a record.

Find $\frac{1}{2}$ of $\frac{1}{3} =$

Show $\frac{1}{2}$

Combine and show
cross product.

Show $\frac{1}{3}$

Find $\frac{1}{2}$ of $\frac{3}{4} =$

Show $\frac{1}{2}$

Combine and show
cross product.

Show $\frac{3}{4}$

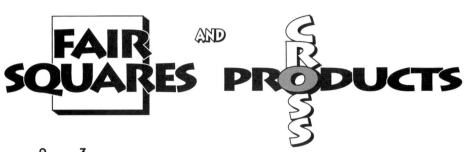

Find $\frac{2}{3}$ of $\frac{3}{4}$ =

Show $\frac{2}{3}$

Combine and show cross product.

Show $\frac{3}{4}$

Looking back.

How are all the squares alike?
Why is this important?

How do cross products help you understand
multiplication of fractions?

CROSS PRODUCTS

$$\frac{1}{2} \times \frac{3}{4} =$$

Use your AIMS Fractional Transparencies to find the products. Use two colors and the frame to make a record of your learning.

$$\frac{1}{3} \times \frac{1}{2} =$$

$$\frac{3}{4} \times \frac{2}{3} =$$

$$\frac{1}{4} \times \frac{1}{6} =$$

$$\frac{2}{5} \times \frac{2}{3} =$$

CROSS PRODUCTS

$$\frac{1}{3} \times \frac{5}{6} =$$

$$\frac{3}{4} \times \frac{3}{5} =$$

$$\frac{2}{3} \times \frac{5}{6} =$$

$$\frac{1}{4} \times \frac{1}{3} =$$

$$\frac{2}{5} \times \frac{1}{2} =$$

A Commentary on the
Division of Fractions

It is difficult to understand why division of fractions is included in the elementary school curriculum. Not only are connections to real-world applications terribly contrived, it is difficult to find a way to build conceptual understanding about the invert and multiply rule. Consequently teachers tell students to "just do it." This practice leads to the meaningless application of a rote procedure and compounds opportunities for mistakes and students' inability to determine why.

While division of fractions is not easily taught, the meaning of division of fractions can be facilitated through problems in context where students use manipulatives to visualize the solution. It is essential that we separate what division of fractions means from what to do with the operation of division of fractions.

Understanding the meaning of the operation using manipulatives

Understanding the meaning of division of fractions with manipulatives is essential. Fractions are difficult for students in large part because students are asked to abstract concepts and procedures before they can picture them or understand them. Therefore using models such as the circle/sector model, fraction fringe model, and the unit square model should be used extensively to solve problems that fit the model.

If division is a process of partitioning or separating into sets or groups or determining how many groups are part of the whole, we need to see how this idea can be applied to situations where the sets are fractions.

Consider $\frac{3}{4}$ divided by $\frac{1}{2}$. Think about $\frac{3}{4}$ using the circle. We can determine how many $\frac{1}{2}$-sized pieces are contained in the larger piece by covering $\frac{3}{4}$ of the circle with $\frac{1}{2}$ and observing that it takes 1 and $\frac{1}{2}$. Not only is this reasonable to see, an answer is produced in simplest terms! Included here is a set of division problems written for use with manipulatives so that students can see to make sense of the problem. (see *Divide and Conquer*). The problems are made more interesting in a context and they include mixed numbers divided by a fraction because they simply are more believable.

Visualizing an algorithm that makes sense

Building on students' prior knowledge about division, we need to ask ourselves about the forms in which students have had experience seeing the abstract representation of division of whole numbers. Most frequently they have seen the dividend under a division sign with the divisor in front of it as pictured.

When asked to read this, students say, "Twelve divided by 3." or "Three *goes into* 12." When asked what this problem means, they may respond that it asks how many threes are in 12. (See *a*.)

a.

$3\overline{)12}$

Another form in which this problem may occur is 12 over 3 as a fraction. In which case students may say twelve-thirds or 12 divided by 3. (See *b*.)

If we replace the whole numbers in each of two examples with fractions, we may get a glimpse of how we could make a reasonable connection to a student's thinking. Suppose we wanted to look at $\frac{7}{8}$ divided by $\frac{3}{8}$.

Students could understand the nature of the problem (how many $\frac{3}{8}$ are in $\frac{7}{8}$) and they could "do" the problem in the same traditional way they divide whole numbers and get a reasonable answer. (2 and $\frac{1}{3}$) The difficulty, by the way, is with the remainder in this problem. One-eighth of the three-eighths is one-third! (See *c*.)

Or we could look at $\frac{3}{4}$ divided by $\frac{1}{2}$ and write $\frac{3}{4}$ as the numerator of the fraction and $\frac{1}{2}$ as the denominator. (See *d*.)

This becomes a problem because we really do not like the "look" of a fraction as the denominator. We really prefer a denominator of 1. If we use the big idea of ONE and multiply both the numerator and the denominator by another expression for ONE, we can make the denominator ONE.

In this case, express ONE as $\frac{2}{1}$ over $\frac{2}{1}$ and multiply both numerator ($\frac{3}{4}$) and denominator ($\frac{1}{2}$) by $\frac{2}{1}$ and you effectively, make the denominator ONE and multiply the numerator by the reciprocal (or inverse) of the denominator. (See *e*.)

Trusting the algorithm

At some point, being able to visualize concretely the division of some fractions becomes too complex for elementary students. If we have encouraged the use of manipulatives to understand simple problems, we may be able now to help students to trust the algorithm to work with more complex problems too.

b. $\frac{12}{3}$

c. $\frac{3}{8} \overline{\smash{)}\begin{array}{r} 2 \\ \frac{7}{8} \\ -\frac{6}{8} \\ \hline \frac{1}{8} \end{array}}$

d. $\dfrac{\frac{3}{4}}{\frac{1}{2}}$

e. $\dfrac{\frac{3}{4}}{\frac{1}{2}} = \dfrac{\frac{3}{4} \times \frac{2}{1}}{\frac{1}{2} \times \frac{2}{1}} = \dfrac{\frac{6}{4}}{1} = 1\frac{1}{2}$

DIVIDE AND CONQUER

Find the answers to these problems using models that make sense to you. Draw a picture that shows your thinking and the model you used. Choose one and explain it to a friend.

$3\frac{3}{4} \div \frac{3}{8} =$

The Murphys had a party and had 3 and $\frac{3}{4}$ pizzas left over. The kids decided they could invite friends over the next day for cold pizza. They figured each friend would eat $\frac{3}{8}$ of a pizza. How many people could be fed?

A group of students were decorating packages for delivery to elderly patients at a convalescent home. They needed $\frac{1}{4}$ yard of ribbon for each package. They had only $4\frac{1}{2}$ yards of ribbon left. How many packages could they decorate?

$4\frac{1}{2} \div \frac{1}{4} =$

$2\frac{3}{4} \div \frac{1}{2} =$

Two students were trying to figure out how many half-hour TV shows they could watch after school before dinner between 3:15 and 6 PM. Can you help them?

Possible Pictures, Solutions, and Discussion

Murphy problem

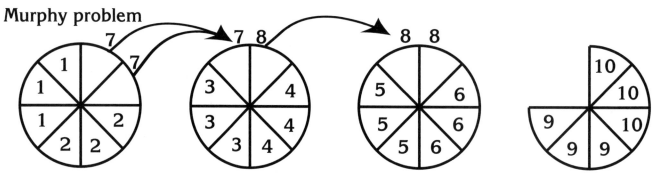

Using the circle model students could describe feeding two people from each whole pizza (6 people altogether) with two pieces left over from each whole pizza (6 pieces) which would feed 2 more people. In addition, 2 more people could be fed from the $\frac{3}{4}$ pizza thus feeding 10 people altogether.

Ribbon Problem

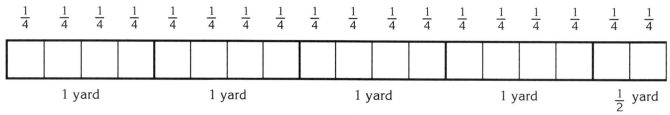

One solution is to use a linear model and simply lay out $4\frac{1}{2}$ yards and then partition each yard into fourths. Count fourths to determine the number of lengths of ribbon. Eighteen packages could be wrapped.

T.V. Problem

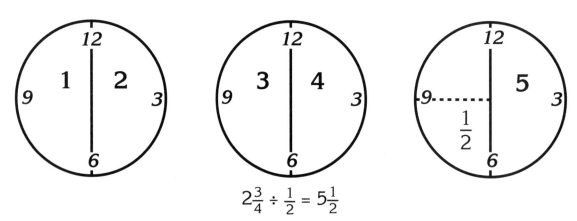

$$2\frac{3}{4} \div \frac{1}{2} = 5\frac{1}{2}$$

Students may connect their understanding of the circle/sector model to a clock face and determine how many half-hours are in $2\frac{3}{4}$ hours. $(5\frac{1}{2})$

Topic
Fractions
Equivalency
Graphing fractions on a coordinate plane

Learning Goals
- To represent and interpret fractions by graphing them as ordered pairs on a coordinate plane
- To explore relative magnitude of fractions
- To examine equivalent fractions and relationships

Guiding Document
NCTM Standards 2000*
- Use models, benchmarks, and equivalent forms to judge the size of fractions
- Use visual models, benchmarks, and equivalent forms to add and subtract commonly used fractions and decimals

Materials
For each student:
square dot paper
colored pencils
straight edge or ruler

For each small group of students:
1 13 x 13-hole pegboard
37 golf tees (one green tee and 6 in six colors—yellow, natural, red, blue, orange, and black)

Background Information
Fractional numbers are graphed on the coordinate plane using ordered pairs corresponding to the denominator and numerator of selected fractions. Using square dot paper, the value of the denominator is located on the horizontal axis and the numerator on the vertical axis and the intersection of these two points is marked on the plane. The experience is similar to locating targets in the children's game "Battleship" in which players identify positions in a field by moving horizontally from a point of origin and then vertically to a particular spot.

The interesting context of this lesson is that it uses a 13 by 13-hole pegboard representing a golf green. Golf tees represent the fractions, each with a unique location on the golf green. Students then transfer the information displayed on the golf green to square dot paper to represent a field of fractions.

Management
1. If possible, paint pegboard squares green to fit the golf scenario of the lesson and provide a background on which the colors of tees will appear more vivid.
2. Tees are easiest to contain and distribute if they are enclosed in zipper-type plastic bags.

Procedure
Part One: Fractions on the Starting Green
1. Distribute a pegboard and 37 tees to each small group of students.
2. Have them find and mark the starting tee (0, 0) with a green tee.
3. Inform them that all moves (tee steps) on the green begin at the starting tee and move across the horizontal axis the number of units represented by the first number in the ordered pair, and then vertically the number of holes represented by the second number in the ordered pair. A tee is placed at that intersection.
4. Direct the students to use yellow tees and place a tee in every hole that represents the ordered pair (2, 1) beginning with the starting tee and moving across the board—over two and up one. Have them repeat this move over and over until all possible intersections are identified with a yellow tee.

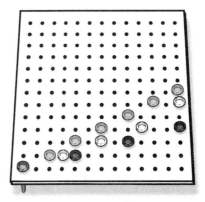

5. Now have them use red tees and place a tee in every hole that marks 3, 1 (over three, up one). Remind the students to always begin at the starting tee and continue the same move across the board.
6. Have students repeat the procedure using these tees and tee-steps:
   Black tees (4, 1): Tee step—Over 4, Up 1.
   Blue tees (6, 1): Tee step—Over 6, Up 1.
   Natural tees (10, 1): Tee step—Over 10, Up 1.
   Orange tees (12, 1): Tee step—Over 12, Up 1.

Discussion

Part One: Fractions on the Starting Green

1. How is any tee related to the next tee of the same color? [It's just a tee-step away! The move or step from one tee to the next tee of the same color is equal to the ordered pair of numbers resulting from that fraction in lowest terms. For example, $\frac{2}{4}$ is related to $\frac{3}{6}$ by a move of (2, 1) or $\frac{1}{2}$.]

2. Each successive tee placement on a diagonal is farther from the starting tee. How does that help us understand equivalent expressions? [Each successive tee is farther from the starting tee and thus can be named in terms of ordered pairs. For example, $\frac{4}{8}$ is (8, 4) or 8 steps across and 4 steps up from the starting tee; and 2 steps across and 1 step up from the previous tee.]

Procedure

Part Two: Score Card

1. Tell the students that they will now need to fill out their *Score Card*. Inform them that they will need to mark the starting hole at the lower left corner in green. (Circle the dot that represents (0,0).)

2. Direct them to count and record the number of each hole on the horizontal and vertical axes.

3. Allow time for the students to record all tee placements found on the pegboard (golf green) in matching colors on the *Score Card* by circling each dot in the corresponding color.

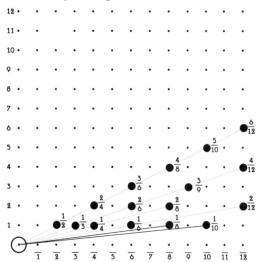

4. Have the students use a straight edge or ruler to join all points of the same color through the starting tee.

5. Have them record the fraction value of each colored tee on the *Score Card*.

Discussion

Part Two: Score Card

1. What is significant about each horizontal row of holes? [Any row of holes names the numerator of a fraction.]

2. What do all the fractions along a colored diagonal line have in common? [They are equivalent fractions.]

3. Name the fractions from the red tees in order from the starting tee.

4. Describe several patterns you observed on your *Score Card*. [Many patterns exist such as numerators are counting numbers; denominators are multiples, etc.]

5. What do the holes in each column of holes have in common? [The column number is the denominator of all fractions in that column.]

6. Use this knowledge to add like fractions such as $\frac{2}{3}$ and $\frac{2}{3}$. Explain to another student how could find the tee placement that marks this sum. [The sum is $\frac{4}{3}$ and is in the column numbered 3 which matches the denominator.]

7. How could you add unlike fractions such as $\frac{1}{2}$ and $\frac{2}{3}$? [Find the diagonal line for $\frac{1}{2}$ and also the diagonal for $\frac{2}{3}$ and move along BOTH lines from the point of origin until a hole or point in both lines occurs in the same numbered column—thus finding a common denominator. In this example, $\frac{3}{6}$ and $\frac{4}{6}$ will be the resulting fractions with a common denominator.]

Procedure

Part Three: A Tee-Table

1. Have students record the fractions for each tee placement in the *Tee-Table* provided.

Discussion

Part Three:

A Tee-Table

1. What do you notice about the fractions in each row that are closest to the tee? [These fractions are expressed in lowest terms.]

Tee Color	2	3	4	5	6	7	8	9	10	11	12
Orange											$\frac{1}{12}$
Natural									$\frac{1}{10}$		
Blue					$\frac{1}{6}$						
Black			$\frac{1}{4}$				$\frac{2}{8}$				$\frac{3}{12}$
Red		$\frac{1}{3}$			$\frac{2}{6}$			$\frac{3}{9}$			$\frac{4}{12}$
Yellow	$\frac{1}{2}$		$\frac{2}{4}$		$\frac{3}{6}$		$\frac{4}{8}$		$\frac{5}{10}$		$\frac{6}{12}$

Columns from Score Card

Evaluation

This multiple representation of fractions on a coordinate plane is most appropriate for upper elementary and middle school students. Therefore, it is recommended that its evaluation is best gathered by listening carefully to students as they respond to the discussion questions such as those posed here.

How are the golf green, the *Score Card*, and the *Tee-Table* similar?

Which form is most meaningful for you in understanding fraction relationships? Explain.

* Reprinted with permission from *Principles and Standards for School Mathematics*, 2000 by the National Council of Teachers of Mathematics. All rights reserved.

Score Card

12 • • • • • • • • • • • •
11 • • • • • • • • • • • •
10 • • • • • • • • • • • •
9 • • • • • • • • • • • •
8 • • • • • • • • • • • •
7 • • • • • • • • • • • •
6 • • • • • • • • • • • •
5 • • • • • • • • • • • •
4 • • • • • • • • • • • •
3 • • • • • • • • • • • •
2 • • • • • • • • • • • •
1 • • • • • • • • • • • •

• • • • • • • • • • • • •
$\overline{1}$ $\overline{2}$ $\overline{3}$ $\overline{4}$ $\overline{5}$ $\overline{6}$ $\overline{7}$ $\overline{8}$ $\overline{9}$ $\overline{10}$ $\overline{11}$ $\overline{12}$

1. Mark the starting hole (0,0) at the lower left corner by circling the dot in green.
2. Count and record all tee placements on the pegboard in matching colors on the Score Card by circling each dot in the corresponding color.
3. Use a straight edge or ruler to join all points of the same color through the starting tee.
4. Record the fraction value of each circled dot on the Score Card.
5. Describe several patterns you observed.

A Tee-Table

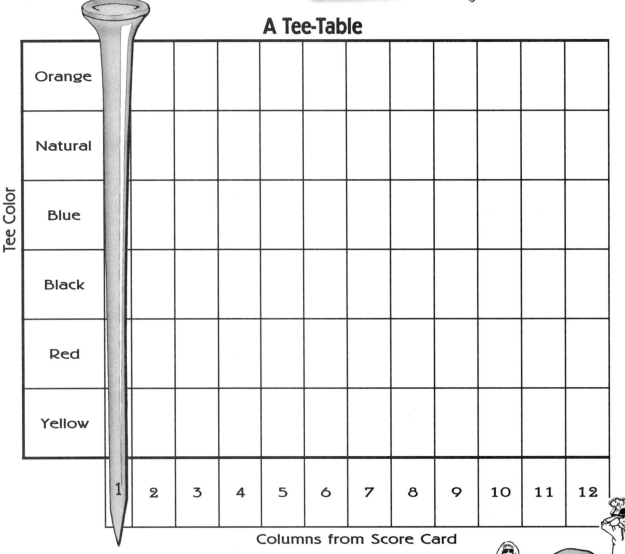

Tee Color	1	2	3	4	5	6	7	8	9	10	11	12
Orange												
Natural												
Blue												
Black												
Red												
Yellow												

Columns from Score Card

1. Record the fraction value of each circled dot from the Score Card in the chart above.

2. What do you notice about the fractions in each row that are closest to the tee?

Fractions with Pattern Blocks

Topic
Fractions
  Meaning of
  Pattern blocks as an area model for fraction concepts
  Equivalencies
  Addition of fractions
  Mixed numbers

Learning Goals
- To use pattern blocks as an area model for recognizing and naming fractions
- To explore the relative sizes of pattern blocks as fractional parts of a whole
- To use pattern blocks to explore equivalent fractions, addition of fractions and mixed number concepts

Guiding Document
NCTM Standards 2000*
- *Develop understanding of fractions as parts of unit wholes, as parts of a collection, as locations on number lines, and as divisions of whole numbers*
- *Use models, benchmarks, and equivalent forms to judge the size of fractions*
- *Recognize and generate equivalent forms of commonly used fractions, decimals, and percents*
- *Work flexibly with fractions, decimals, and percents to solve problems*

Materials
Selected pattern blocks—yellow hexagons, red trapezoids, green triangles, blue rhombi, brown trapezoids, and purple right triangles
Construction paper models of these pieces
Large chart paper
Colored pencils
Colored marking pens
Scissors
Black construction paper, $3\frac{1}{2}$ x 5 inches
Glue
Index cards, 5" x 8"

Background Information
The standard pattern block set contains the hexagon, isosceles trapezoid, rhombus, equilateral triangle. Two new pieces have been created by the AIMS Education Foundation: a trapezoid that is half of the isosceles trapezoid and a right triangle that is one-twelfth of the hexagon. These six pieces lend themselves nicely as parts of an area model for fractions such as $\frac{1}{2}$, $\frac{1}{3}$, $\frac{1}{4}$, $\frac{1}{6}$, and $\frac{1}{12}$.

These pattern blocks are especially useful in the development of a student's ability to recognize and name equivalent fractions and to explore fraction relationships among all of the blocks.

Because of the tactile nature of the pattern blocks, students may manipulate the pieces as they look for solutions to the questions suggested. Furthermore, the pattern blocks contribute a sense of playfulness to the experience thus enriching it and increasing the likelihood of it being remembered and useful.

This activity begins with an exploration of all the possible relationships blocks may have to each other and then moves to assigning the yellow hexagon a value of ONE for some problem-solving experiences with mixed numbers and addition of fractions.

Management
1. Prepare a tub or box of six kinds of pattern blocks for each small group of students making sure that there are more of each piece than are needed to construct the whole (hexagon). For example, four to six trapezoids rather than just two to make one whole.
2. Prepare ahead of time construction paper models of the same pattern block pieces so that students can paste a permanent copy of their quilt pieces. (See *That's Sum Quilt.*) The Ellison die cut has dies for producing these pieces easily except for the two new pieces. These can be made by using brown paper for the isosceles trapezoid and then using scissors to cut these pieces in half. The purple triangle can be made by cutting equilateral triangles from purple paper and cutting them in half again.

Procedure
1. Distribute to each small group a tub of pattern blocks. Ask students to select one color block and find other smaller, identical blocks to cover the larger one. For example, two red trapezoids will cover one yellow hexagon. Ask students to discuss how the red block is part of the larger yellow one.
2. Continue this exploration by trying to find all the different relationships of one or more identical

69

blocks to any larger block. Each block is presented by a letter that corresponds to its color. For example, r=red, bl=blue, br=brown, p=purple, y=yellow, and g=green. Show them how to use chart paper to record these relationships as fractions and also to illustrate them.

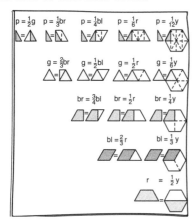

(See *Solutions* for other relationships)

3. Ask students to explain and justify their drawings and fraction sentences.

4. In *Picturing Mixed Numbers*, direct students to create a design with pattern blocks according to a set of instructions described in the activity. Instructions are to create a design in an empty frame using a fixed number of blocks in such a way that the total value of the design is equal to a mixed number. Students should then write a number sentence that shows how the collection of like colored blocks as fractions can be added to show the total value. Have students share their designs and see how many different ways they were able to picture these mixed numbers.

5. For *Mixed Number Riddles*, distribute to each student the activity page on which students fill-in the black-line perimeters according to the rules of the riddle–a fixed number of colors and blocks, and a total value. After trying the two that are pictured, distribute 5" x 8" index cards and invite students to design their own riddles. Trade with a neighbor to solve.

6. The final activity, *That's Sum Quilt*, is an invitation to design a quilt piece using pattern blocks on a black construction paper mat that measures $3\frac{1}{2}$ x 5 inches. Two choices are suggested: combinations of red, brown, purple, and yellow OR combinations of blue, green, purple, and yellow. Direct the students to determine the total value of the quilt piece by finding the sum of the parts.

Invite then to use colored paper pieces to make a copy of the quilt piece designed with the blocks. Collect the quilt pieces and combine into a large wall mural.

7. As a class, compare the different sums and patterns. (It works well to have a group of four students plan and create four quilt pieces that are the same and put them together to form a larger quilt piece.)

Discussion

1. How did you know what fraction name to give to a pattern block as you were covering a larger block with smaller ones? [The number of identical pieces it takes to cover a larger piece determines its value. For instance, two red trapezoids cover a yellow hexagon. Therefore, r= $\frac{1}{2}$ y].

2. Which pattern block pieces had more than one "name" or fraction expression? Why? [larger pieces because they could be covered by different blocks in many ways.]

3. How many different fraction relationships could you find? (Answers will vary according to students efforts.)

4. How could you explain to someone new to the study of fractions, the meaning of the numerator and denominator in a fraction using the pattern block pieces? [The numerator indicates the number of pieces being considered; the denominator indicates the total number of pieces it takes to cover the whole.]

5. Choose one picture frame or the other in *Picturing Mixed Numbers* and share with your neighbor how you were able to combine pattern blocks to get a total of $2\frac{1}{2}$ or $1\frac{1}{3}$.

6. Compare two frames with the same value but different combinations of blocks. How are they alike or different?

7. How would the designs in these frames differ if you were using four colors instead of three? Try it and share with a neighbor.

8. Compare your solution for one of the *Mixed Number Riddles* with a friend. Are the solutions the same or different? Explain. How many different solutions were generated in the classroom? Is it possible to find more? Explain.

9. Compare the quilt pieces generated by others in your group or class. Are there any identical pieces? How are the "sums" the same or different? What is the range of the sums? What is the highest and lowest sum? What sums in-between could be generated?

10. Design another fraction piece that could be added to the pattern block set. Why did you choose that one?

Extensions

1. Have the students use a tangram puzzle to create a fraction design, letting the sum of the pieces have a value of one whole. Direct them to determine the value of each tangram piece. Encourage them to create a variety of designs.

2. Have students use pattern blocks to tessellate a plane surface. Are there any pattern blocks that will not tessellate? Why?

Solutions

Pattern Block Relationships

$r = \frac{1}{2}y$ two reds cover one yellow

$g = \frac{1}{2}bl$ two greens cover one blue

$g = \frac{1}{3}r$ three greens cover one red

$g = \frac{1}{6}y$ six greens cover one yellow

$br = \frac{1}{4}y$ four browns cover one yellow

$br = \frac{1}{2}r$ two browns cover one red

$bl = \frac{1}{3}y$ three blues cover one yellow

$p = \frac{1}{12}y$ twelve purples cover one yellow

$p = \frac{1}{6}r$ six purples cover one red

$p = \frac{1}{3}br$ three purples cover one brown

$p = \frac{1}{2}g$ two purples cover one green

Picturing Mixed Numbers

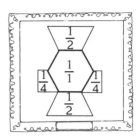

Solution to $2\frac{1}{2} = 1 + \frac{2}{2} + \frac{2}{4} = 2\frac{1}{2}$

Solution to $1\frac{2}{3} = \frac{1}{2} + \frac{5}{6} + \frac{1}{3}$

Mixed Number Riddles

1. $\frac{4}{4}$ (brown) + $\frac{4}{12}$ (purple) + $\frac{2}{3}$ (blue)

2. $\frac{4}{6}$ (green) + $\frac{3}{3}$ (blue) + $\frac{4}{12}$ (purple)

Evidence of Learning

Any part of the experiences described could be used for evaluation of learning and understanding. Because there is so much exploration, there are many opportunities for the teacher to observe a variety of solutions and listen as students explain their thinking. This kind of evaluation is informal and relies to a great extent on the teacher's intuition and willingness to probe a student's thinking by asking good questions as they are working.

Having students write out fraction relationships using symbols as well as pictures helps the second language learners connect new ideas and new language.

*   Reprinted with permission from *Principles and Standards for School Mathematics*, 2000 by the National Council of Teachers of Mathematics. All rights reserved.

Picturing Mixed Numbers

Let the yellow hexagon equal one. Use three colors of pattern blocks. Make a design that has a total value of $2\frac{1}{2}$. Label the blocks.

Write a number sentence that shows the addition of like colored blocks.

Number sentence:

2½

Try another. Use three colors to make a design worth $1\frac{2}{3}$.
Number sentence:

1⅔

72

MIXED NUMBER RIDDLES

Use 10 pattern blocks in 3 colors to make a total value of 2.

Fill me in!

Use 11 blocks in 3 colors to make a total value of 2.

Design your own riddle on a 5" x 8" index card.
Trade with a neighbor to solve.

That's Sum Quilt!

Use pattern blocks to create a quilt piece. Try red, brown, purple and yellow blocks. Then use colored construction paper to create the quilt piece on a black construction paper mat ($3\frac{1}{2}$" x 5").

Sum of the parts:

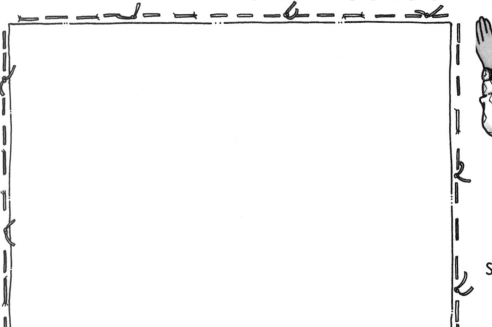

Now try blue, green, purple, and yellow pattern blocks.

Sum of the parts:

Topic
Fractions
  Proportional reasoning
  Equivalency

Learning Goals
- To use tangram pieces as an area model for the study of fractions
- To explore the fractional relationships among the tangram pieces

Guiding Documents
NCTM Standards 2000*
- *Investigate relationships among fractions, decimals, and percents*
- *Recognize and generate equivalent forms of commonly used fractions, decimals, and percents*
- *Use models, benchmarks, and equivalent forms to judge the size of fractions*

Materials
4 -5 sets of the tangram puzzle in five different colors (for each group of 4-5 students)
1 10-cm square of black construction paper for each student (for coverlet)
1 10-cm square of colored construction paper for each student (for cutting)
Scissors
Glue stick

Background Information
Students need to have many and varied experiences with recognizing fractional parts in the real world in order to build a strong conceptual base and visual referents. Many activities involving a variety of appropriate manipulatives and objects should be utilized to build a solid understanding so that when operations with fractional numbers are undertaken, students will have a mental image of what is transpiring.

In this activity, the 10 cm square serves as an area model in which the tangram pieces are used to cover the whole square. The large triangle represents $\frac{1}{4}$ of the square, the medium triangle, the square, and the parallelogram each represent $\frac{1}{8}$; and each of the two small triangles $\frac{1}{16}$. Students need to understand that the numerator tells how many pieces are under discussion and that the denominator describes the kind or size of the pieces being considered.

Students may have had some experience with tangram puzzles. Nevertheless, it is still beneficial to have them follow oral directions for cutting the 10 cm square into the seven tangram pieces.

Management
1. It is worthwhile to read *Grandfather Tang's Story* by Ann Tompert (Crown Publishers, 1990) or *The Warlord's Puzzle* by Walton Pilegard (Pelican Publishing Co., 2000) as an introduction to this activity.
2. It is also helpful to make many sets of the tangram puzzle out of brightly colored construction paper or colored vinyl placemats using the Ellison cutting machine.

Procedure
1. Read one of the book selections suggested above to introduce the idea of a tangram puzzle.

Part One: Folding and Cutting the Tangram
Tangrammy Squares provides the opportunity for students to fold and cut the 10 cm square into the seven tangram pieces and then name the fractional part of each piece when the whole square has an area of ONE.
1. Distribute one 10 cm square of colored construction paper to each student. Provide instructions for cutting the seven tangram pieces.

Steps for Cutting the Seven Tangram Pieces

1. Fold 10 cm square in half along a diagonal. Cut along the crease.
2. Take one of the halves, fold it in half again and cut along the crease. The square has now been cut into three pieces, one is half and the other two are fourths.
3. Take the remaining half (large triangle) and fold it so that the vertex of the right angle touches the midpoint of the opposite side and cut along the crease thus producing a small triangle and a trapezoid. Set the triangle aside.
4. Take the trapezoid, fold it in half and cut along the crease to produce two trapezoids of the same size and shape.
5. Fold and cut one of the trapezoids to produce a triangle and a square.
6. Fold and cut the other trapezoid to produce a triangle and a parallelogram.

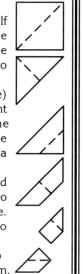

2. Have students use the seven tangram pieces and reconstruct the original square.

Part Two: Exploring Equivalent Fractions
   Tangram Trading Post is an open-ended opportunity for students to post or picture all the possible relationships that can be found using tangram pieces.
1. Ask students to find all the ways each tangram piece is part of the complete tangram square and also how pieces can be traded for smaller tangram pieces.
2. Have them label all trades by showing how fractions are part of the relationship. For instance, one medium triangle is $\frac{1}{8}$ of the 10 cm square. Two of them cover the large triangle ($\frac{1}{4}$), the equivalent fraction for the large triangle is $\frac{2}{8}$.
3. Direct them to make a chart, table, or poster of their discoveries with pictures and symbols. They can use chart paper or the included student sheet.

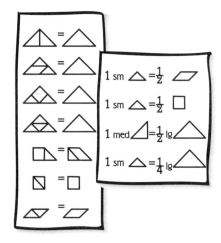

Part Three: Tangrammy Coverlets
1. Inform the students that their task is to design a patchwork piece that uses a 10 cm square of black construction paper with brightly colored tangram pieces. Discuss with them that if each tangram piece has a fractional value, then each patchwork square has a total value of the colored design. Tell them that they may cut any tangram piece in half again in order to produce more variety in size, but they must be able to determine the resulting fractional value.

2. When students have finished their patchwork designs and found the total value of each, have them put them together to form a class coverlet for the wall. As patchwork squares are being added to the coverlet, have students keep a running tally of its added value.

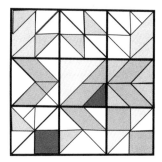

Discussion
1. How did you know what fractional name to give a tangram piece? [by recognizing its relationship to the whole]
2. How is the denominator of any fraction related to the complete square? [It names the size of the piece or the number it takes to cover the whole.]
3. What role does the numerator play? [number of pieces considered]
4. How many equivalent fractions were we able to find? What does it mean to say that they are equivalent?[They have the same area.]

Evaluation
   Each patchwork coverlet piece created by a student in *Part Three* provides an opportunity for students to further explain the relationship of tangram parts to the whole.

Evidence of Learning
1. Listen for accurate representations of each part represented in the coverlet.
2. Look for insight and creativity in the coverlet pieces.

* Reprinted with permission from *Principles and Standards for School Mathematics,* 2000 by the National Council of Teachers of Mathematics. All rights reserved.

Tangrammy Squares

Tangrammy Trading Post: Post your trades here.

Topic
Fractions
    Circle/sector model
    Circle/pie graphs

Learning Goals
* To recognize fractions in real-world problems or situations
* To represent and interpret fractions in a circle or pie graph
* To recognize the relative size of fractions

Guiding Document
NCTM Standard 2000*
* *Work flexibly with fractions, decimals, and percents to solve problems*

Materials
For each group of three or four students:
    one AIMS Fraction Circle Model
    scissors
    glue
    colored pencils, optional

Background Information
In this activity three situations are described in which the results of a class survey are reported. Students are asked to match the appropriate graph with each problem. Two graphs remain unused and students are to select one and write a story using fractions that illustrates the problem.

Management
1. In this lesson it is important for students to be encouraged to talk to each other about how they make sense of the problem and its appropriate matching circle graph. Instead of being concerned about finding common denominators, encourage a discussion about how many parts are represented in the problem and how those parts compare. For instance, is one part much larger than the others? Are any parts the same size? Are all the

parts different? The lesson is intended to magnify the importance of understanding the relative size of fractions and corresponding graphic representation. It is not intended to be a lesson about common denominators and expressing fractions in lowest terms.
2. This lesson is also directed at pointing out to students that many test situations are more easily solved by understanding the big idea and being able to recognize the relative size of fractions over just being able to find a common denominator and add or perform some other operation.

Procedure
1. Distribute to each small group of students a set of fraction wholes and parts. Explain that they will be using these models to solve some problems.
2. Distribute the problems reporting survey data in *Talking in Circles* and the accompanying circle graphs.
3. Ask students to read the three situations and be ready to raise questions if there are any parts of the problems that the group does not understand. While the first two problems usually are clear, the third problem poses some difficulty because students do not recognize that "most" refers to just 14 students and that "most" also means more than half.
4. Clarify with students that as a group they are to find the circle graph that matches each of the first three problems, cut it out and glue it, or copy it, next to the appropriate problem. If they wish to add color to the graphs, they may do so. Then groups should be prepared to explain how they arrived at their solutions as part of a class discussion.
5. At this point, explain that two graphs remain unused. Direct each student in the group to select one of the remaining graphs and to write an original story to match the graph.
6. Take time to share stories and graphs that students designed on their own.
7. Ask students to write problems and then exchange with others to prepare a graph that matches the story.

Discussion
1. Which problems give you clear information that is helpful in choosing an appropriate graph? [Probably #1 and #2 because both problems refer to parts of groups in fraction form.]
2. What kinds of misunderstanding might occur in problem #3? (The word "most" followed parenthetically by (14) is a source of some confusion. In this case, most is 14 which means that more than half of the class numbers 14. When added to the other two numbers, 6 and 4, one can determine that there are 24 in the class. Although, this information is not necessary to solve the problem, students may notice that there are three parts of the whole

identified and that none of the parts are identical. One part is slightly more than half and the other two parts are different, smaller, and together do not make a half of the whole.)

Evaluation

Talking in Circles could provide on-going information about a student's understanding of the relative size of fractions and also of his or her ability to apply that knowledge in interpreting circle or pie graphs.

The evaluation could take place in two parts—one for group processing and one for individual performance. For example, the first three situations providing survey data could serve as a group project while the last problem is an opportunity for students to show further insight in creating their own situation to match a given graph.

Evidence of Learning

1. Watch for appropriate matching of graph to problem.
2. Listen for reasonable explanations of thinking about how decisions were made in choosing the "right" graph. For instance, were students able to make clear their understanding that two fractions were the same in the problem so that two parts of the circle graph were also the same?
3. Listen for logical explanations that show students were able to generalize ideas about relative size of fractions. For example, "most" means more than half, so I was looking for a graph that showed a large part greater than half.

Talking in Circles

1. In a class survey of favorite ice cream flavors, $\frac{2}{3}$ liked cookies and creme, $\frac{1}{6}$ liked peanut butter and chocolate, and $\frac{1}{6}$ liked chunky fudge.

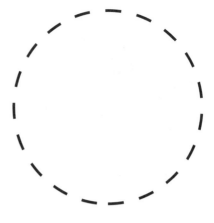

2. In a school-wide vote about cafeteria food for the last day of school, $\frac{3}{4}$ of the students preferred pepperoni pizza while $\frac{1}{8}$ of the students wanted hamburgers and $\frac{1}{8}$ wanted tacos.

3. In a fifth-grade class, most (14) of the students walk to school, 6 students ride a bike, and 4 students roller blade or skateboard to school.

4. An original problem that matches one of the remaining graphs goes like this:

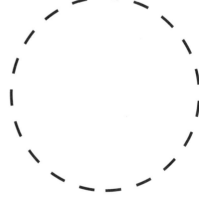

Talking in Circles

Cut and paste or copy the appropriate circle graph with its matching story. Use one of the leftover pictures to write an original problem of your own.

Ice Cream

Topic
Fractions
  Group/ set model
  Circle graph

Learning Goals
- To recognize and name fractions as representative of a counted part of a group or set of objects
- To understand the meaning of numerator and denominator in the symbolic form of a fraction

Guiding Document
NCTM Standards 2000*
- *Develop number sense for fractions and decimals*
- *Develop concepts of fractions, mixed numbers and decimals*
- *Understand, represent and use numbers in a variety of equivalent forms (integer, fraction, decimal)*
- *Develop number sense for whole numbers, fractions, decimals*

Materials
For each student or pair of students:
  one paper cup (3 oz. bathroom size)
  12 jelly beans of 3-4 colors
  colored pencils or crayons
  scissors

Background Information
Assorted jelly bean candy such as Jelly Bellys® may be purchased in 8-oz. packages (approx. 200 count) for about $2. These candies are smaller than the regular jelly bean and come in an assortment of 39 or more flavors. Other candies may be used at the discretion of the creative teacher.

Any circle or pie graph may be used to represent a whole set or group of objects having a common characteristic or attribute such as color. A circular region is partitioned into sections or sectors. Each sector represents a part of the whole set of jelly beans. The area of each sector of the graph is proportional to the fraction of the whole set of jelly beans.

In this activity, students draw different sets of jelly beans from a cup of 12 and represent their colors in several circle graphs. Each graph is then summarized using fractions to show their thinking.

Management
1. To keep the fractions interesting with numerators other than one, use no more than three or four colors of jelly beans in a set of 12.
2. Make up cups of 12 jelly beans ahead of time.
3. The activity could be an independent or a paired experience. It is strongly recommended that it be a paired experience to encourage students to explain their thinking to one another for shared learning.
4. If candy is not appropriate in your classroom, think about using colored plastic counting bears or chips, buttons, or other small manipulative that has an easily observed common attribute for sorting.

Procedure
1. Explain that each student or pair of students will be drawing jelly beans from a cup and making a circle or pie graph to show the number and color of jelly beans in a group.
2. Distribute a paper cup with 12 jelly beans to each student or pair of students along with colored pencils.
3. Review instructions with students explaining that they will be making a record of each round by coloring the jelly bean pictures to match the colors in each round and then making a circle graph that corresponds to the colors in the set.
4. Explain that at Round 6 they will be using all (12) jelly beans and they will be organizing and summarizing their data.
5. Clarify for students that with each round, jelly beans may be added to the previous round to make a new set or the jelly beans from one round may be recycled into the cup and a new set generated. For example, in Round 2, you may add one more jelly bean from the cup to make three, or you may return the two to the cup and draw three new ones.
6. Review the activity page, *Jelly Bean Rounds*, explaining that students will select and picture each set, represent the colors of beans in a circle graph, and use fractions to summarize the color distribution. For example, Round 1, if I have one red and one yellow jelly bean, the circle will be divided into two equal parts and colored respectively. To summarize, $\frac{1}{2}$ = red and $\frac{1}{2}$ = yellow.
7. Explain to students that in Round 6 all 12 jelly beans will be used and represented in two ways — grouped by color on a strip of paper and also on a circle graph.
8. Direct them to group the jelly beans by color and to copy that arrangement on the strip provided at the bottom of the page. Have the students cut out the strip and curl it around the circumference of the circle and mark the circle accordingly. Invite them to color in the circle sectors and compare and summarize the data.

Discussion

1. How do the circle graphs relate to the jelly beans? [The circle represents all the jelly beans in a set. The sectors show the number of each color.]

2. Explain how one jelly bean could be a large part of one circular region and a small part of another. [The size of the circle sector for one jelly bean depends on the total number or size of the group. It is proportional to the set. For example, one jelly bean could represent $\frac{1}{2}$ or $\frac{1}{6}$.]

3. How many different ways could four jelly beans be represented in a circle graph? [$\frac{4}{4}$ in one color; $\frac{3}{4}$ in one color, $\frac{1}{4}$ in second color; $\frac{2}{4}$ in one color, $\frac{2}{4}$ in second color; $\frac{1}{4}$ in one color, $\frac{1}{4}$ in second color, $\frac{2}{4}$ in third color; $\frac{1}{4}$ in one color, $\frac{1}{4}$ in second color, $\frac{1}{4}$ in third color, $\frac{1}{4}$ in fourth color.]

4. In a set of 12 jelly beans where 4 jelly beans are red, what are two ways that that ratio can be expressed? [$\frac{4}{12}$ or $\frac{1}{3}$]

Evidence of Learning

1. Look for correspondence between picture, circle graph and fractions.

2. Look for "fair shares" in the circle graph and accurate representation of numerator and denominator.

3. Listen to explanations of students' thinking as they summarize and explain their work.

* Reprinted with permission from *Principles and Standards for School Mathematics,* 2000 by the National Council of Teachers of Mathematics. All rights reserved.

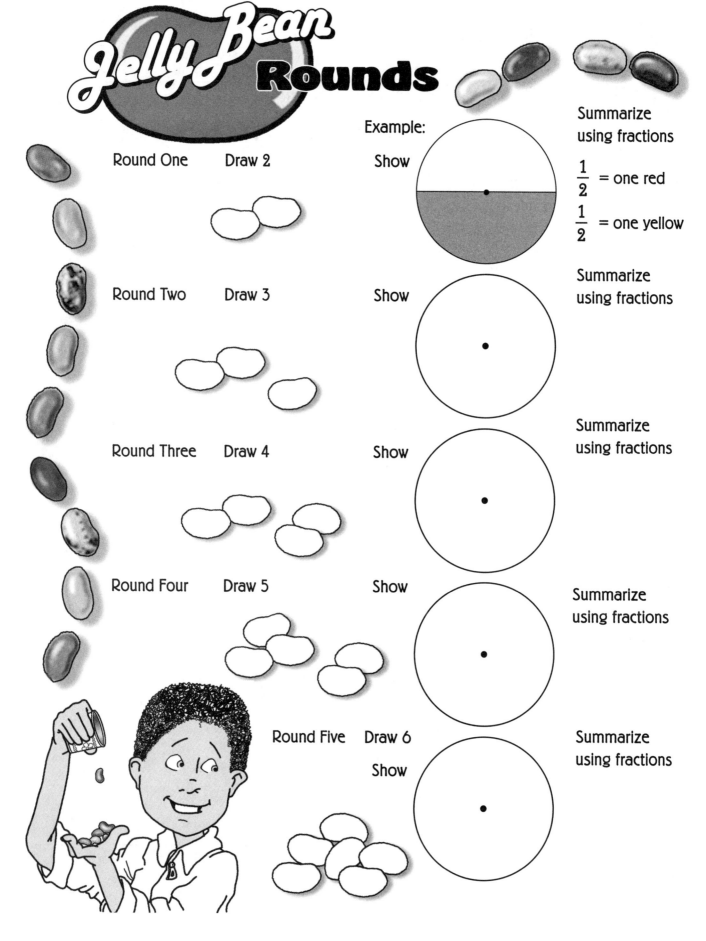

Jelly Bean Rounds

Round One   Draw 2   Show   Example:

Summarize using fractions

$\frac{1}{2}$ = one red

$\frac{1}{2}$ = one yellow

Round Two   Draw 3   Show   Summarize using fractions

Round Three   Draw 4   Show   Summarize using fractions

Round Four   Draw 5   Show   Summarize using fractions

Round Five   Draw 6   Show   Summarize using fractions

Jelly Beans Final Round

Draw 12

Use fractions to describe the jelly beans by color. Tell the story. Compare and generalize the data.

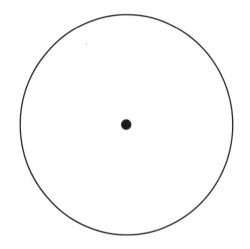

Organize: Sort by color and record on paper strip. Cut and curl to match the circle. Make a circle graph.

B·E·T·W·E·E·N ZERO AND ONE

Topic
Fractions
    Equivalency
    Ordering

Learning Goals
* To provide practice recognizing equivalent fractions
* To practice ordering fractions

Guiding Document
NCTM Standards 2000*
* *Compare and order fractions, decimals, and percents efficiently and find their approximate locations on a number line*
* *Develop number sense for fractions and decimals*
* *Understand, represent, and use numbers in a variety of equivalent forms*

Materials
Set of 48 fraction cards: halves, thirds, fourths, fifths, sixths, eighths, tenths, twelfths, eighteenths, and twenty-fourths.
ZERO card
ONE card

Object of the Game
Be the player with the highest score placing all his/her cards on the table in correct order between ZERO and ONE.

Rules of the Game
1. Place the ZERO card, the one-half card, and the ONE card on the table face-up so that one-half is in the middle and ONE is to the right and ZERO to the left.

2. From the deck of fraction cards, deal five cards to each player. Set the rest of the cards in a pile face down from which each player will replenish his or her hand.
3. In turn each player places a card from his/her hand face up on the table between ZERO and ONE and explains to other players his/her reasoning. If the

card is equivalent to a card already on the table, the new card is placed on top of its equivalent.
4. As play continues the line of fractions grows.
5. Each player scores the number of points in the denominator of the card played.
6. Each player draws a new card from the fraction pool at the end of each play.
7. Play ends when all cards are played.
8. In the event a card is placed incorrectly, the card is removed and the player receives no points for that turn.

Grade Level and Ability Adjustments
Adjust playing deck accordingly:
For beginning learners: (perhaps third and fourth graders)
    Use only halves, fourths, and eighths.

For intermediate learners: (perhaps fourth and fifth graders)
    Use halves, thirds, fourths, fifths, sixths and eighths.

For advanced learners: (perhaps sixth graders and middle school students)
    Use the complete deck that includes additional cards with denominators of 12, 16, 18, 24.

* Reprinted with permission from *Principles and Standards for School Mathematics,* 2000 by the National Council of Teachers of Mathematics. All rights reserved.

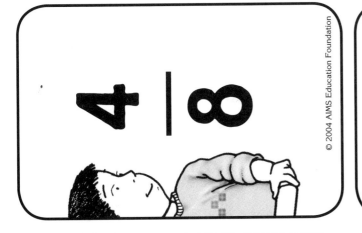

$$\frac{4}{8}$$

$$\frac{12}{24}$$

$$\frac{3}{6}$$

$$\frac{9}{18}$$

$$\frac{2}{4}$$

$$\frac{6}{12}$$

$$\frac{1}{2}$$

$$\frac{5}{10}$$

$$\frac{8}{24}$$

$$\frac{16}{24}$$

$$\frac{4}{12}$$

$$\frac{8}{12}$$

$$\frac{2}{6}$$

$$\frac{4}{6}$$

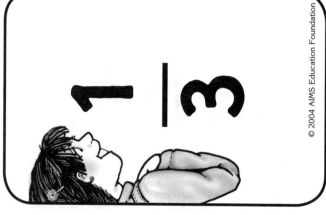

$$\frac{1}{3}$$

$$\frac{2}{3}$$

$$\frac{6}{24}$$

$$\frac{18}{24}$$

$$\frac{3}{12}$$

$$\frac{9}{12}$$

$$\frac{2}{8}$$

$$\frac{6}{8}$$

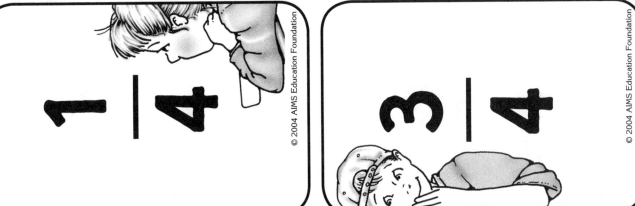

$$\frac{1}{4}$$

$$\frac{3}{4}$$

$$\frac{4}{24}$$

$$\frac{20}{24}$$

$$\frac{3}{18}$$

$$\frac{15}{18}$$

$$\frac{2}{12}$$

$$\frac{10}{12}$$

$$\frac{1}{6}$$

$$\frac{5}{6}$$

$$\frac{4}{10}$$

$$\frac{8}{10}$$

$$\frac{2}{5}$$

$$\frac{4}{5}$$

$$\frac{2}{10}$$

$$\frac{6}{10}$$

$$\frac{1}{5}$$

$$\frac{3}{5}$$

9/24   21/24

3/8   7/8

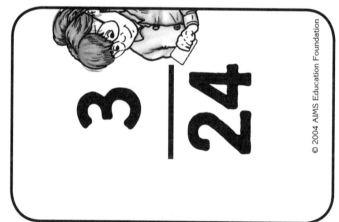

3/24   15/24

1/8   5/8

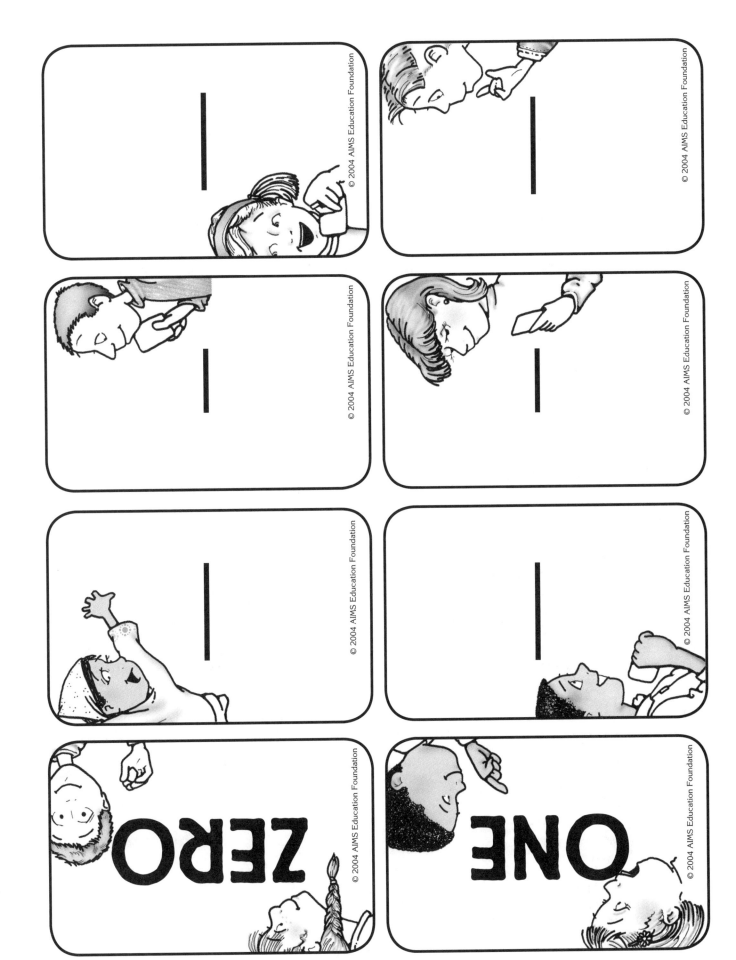

93

Topic
Fractions
    Equivalency
    Part/whole relationships

Learning Goals
- To provide practice recognizing equivalent fractions
- To provide practice recognizing part/whole relationships

Guiding Document
NCTM Standards 2000*
- *Develop number sense for fractions and decimals*
- *Understand, represent, and use numbers in a variety of equivalent forms*

Materials
For each player in independent practice or for each group in group practice:
    one set of 48 equivalent fraction cards

Background Information
Competence and speed in recognizing and naming equivalent fractions enhances a student's ability to perform operations on fractions. Learning a skill requires practice, reinforcement, repetition, and success in different forms and problem-solving settings so that students understand and feel confident in their abilities.

The fractional numbers with halves, thirds, fourths, sixths, eighths, tenths, and twelfths constitute more than 95 percent of the numbers an average student will use in a lifetime. Therefore, these receive primary attention is these practice activities.

Management
Two games, *Fair Pairs* and *One is a Winner,* are described in two formats, one for independent practice and one for group practice.

Procedure
Independent Practice—Fair Pairs
Provide the students with the following directions:
1. Shuffle the cards and place all cards face up in 12 stacks of four cards each.
2. Remove top cards in pairs that name equivalent but not identical fractions.
3. During play, if any stack is emptied, any other stack may be split so that there are always 12 stacks from which to choose.

4. The player wins if all cards are matched correctly. The player loses if at any time none of the 12 cards showing form a matching pair or if a pair is formed that does not name the same fraction.

Independent Practice—One is a Winner
Provide the students with the following directions:
1. Shuffle the cards and distribute exactly like *Fair Pairs* but remove in pairs that add up to ONE.
2. If all pairs are formed correctly, no cards will be left.

Group Practice—Fair Pairs
Provide the students with the following directions:
1. Shuffle the cards and deal four cards to each player and place four face-up on the table. Place the remaining cards in a stack face down from which players can draw.
2. During a turn, a player plays any card from his hand onto the table and then claims all pairs (only pairs) that name the same fraction. Player receives one point for each pair. To complete the turn, the player must draw cards from the face-down stack so that there are always four in his/her hand.
3. The player scoring the highest number of points is the winner.
4. The game is self-correcting if all cards are paired correctly and all cards are used.

Group Practice—One is a Winner
Provide the students with the following directions:
1. This is played just like *Fair Pairs* except that the pairs are made up of two cards whose sum is ONE.

Evidence of Learning
Games are self-correcting. Listen for affective signs that indicate success or frustration.

* Reprinted with permission from *Principles and Standards for School Mathematics,* 2000 by the National Council of Teachers of Mathematics. All rights reserved.

Who Has? For Fractions

A sample set of *Who Has? Fraction* cards is included here for a group of 30 students. The set includes fractions with "friendly" denominators such as halves, thirds, fourths, sixths, eighths, twelfths, and sixteenths and requires that students be able to add and subtract like fractions and to express fractions in equivalent terms. The set that is provided has two blank cards that can be used for designing your own game.

Directions

1. Distribute one card to each student, or several cards to pairs of students.
2. Select a student to begin by reading his/her card aloud—"I have $\frac{3}{4}$, who has that take away $\frac{1}{4}$?"
3. The person holding the answer to the card responds by reading aloud the card with the appropriate response.
4. The game is self-generating and ends when the cycle returns to the beginning card; in this case, $\frac{3}{4}$.

Solution

The full set of fraction cards is listed here to better facilitate the questions and answers in this beginning set of cards. (Note: Answers should be expressed in the same terms as the fractions in the problem unless otherwise directed.)

I have $\frac{3}{4}$. Who has that take away $\frac{1}{4}$?

I have $\frac{2}{4}$. Who has that in lowest terms?

I have $\frac{1}{2}$. Who has that expressed in twelfths?

I have $\frac{6}{12}$. Who has that take away $\frac{2}{12}$?

I have $\frac{4}{12}$. Who has that in lowest terms?

I have $\frac{1}{3}$. Who has that plus $\frac{1}{3}$?

I have $\frac{2}{3}$. Who has that expressed in sixths?

I have $\frac{4}{6}$. Who has that plus $\frac{1}{6}$?

I have $\frac{5}{6}$. Who has that in twelfths?

I have $\frac{10}{12}$. Who has that take away $\frac{3}{12}$?

I have $\frac{7}{12}$. Who has that plus $\frac{2}{12}$?

I have $\frac{9}{12}$. Who has that take away $\frac{8}{12}$?

I have $\frac{1}{12}$. Who has that plus $\frac{7}{12}$?

I have $\frac{8}{12}$. Who has that plus $\frac{3}{12}$?

I have $\frac{11}{12}$. Who has that plus $\frac{1}{12}$?

I have $\frac{12}{12}$, the same as ONE. Who has that take away $\frac{4}{8}$?

I have $\frac{4}{8}$. Who has that plus $\frac{2}{8}$?

I have $\frac{6}{8}$. Who has that take away $\frac{4}{8}$?

I have $\frac{2}{8}$. Who has that expressed in fourths?

I have $\frac{1}{4}$. Who has that plus $\frac{3}{8}$? (hard problem!)

I have $\frac{5}{8}$. Who has that in sixteenths?

I have $\frac{10}{16}$. Who has that take away $\frac{5}{16}$?

I have $\frac{5}{16}$. Who has that plus $\frac{4}{16}$?

I have $\frac{9}{16}$. Who has that take away $\frac{1}{16}$?

I have $\frac{8}{16}$. Who has that plus $\frac{5}{16}$?

I have $\frac{13}{16}$. Who has that plus $\frac{2}{16}$?

I have $\frac{15}{16}$. Who has that take away $\frac{8}{16}$?

I have $\frac{7}{16}$. Who has that take away $\frac{3}{16}$?

I have $\frac{4}{16}$. Who has three times that?

I have $\frac{12}{16}$. Who has that in lowest terms?

I have $\frac{6}{12}$. Who has that take away $\frac{2}{12}$?

I have $\frac{4}{6}$. Who has that plus $\frac{1}{6}$?

I have $\frac{1}{2}$. Who has that expressed in twelfths?

I have $\frac{2}{3}$. Who has that expressed in sixths?

I have $\frac{2}{4}$. Who has that in lowest terms?

I have $\frac{1}{3}$. Who has that plus $\frac{1}{3}$?

I have $\frac{3}{4}$. Who has that take away $\frac{1}{4}$?

I have $\frac{4}{12}$. Who has that in lowest terms?

© AIMS

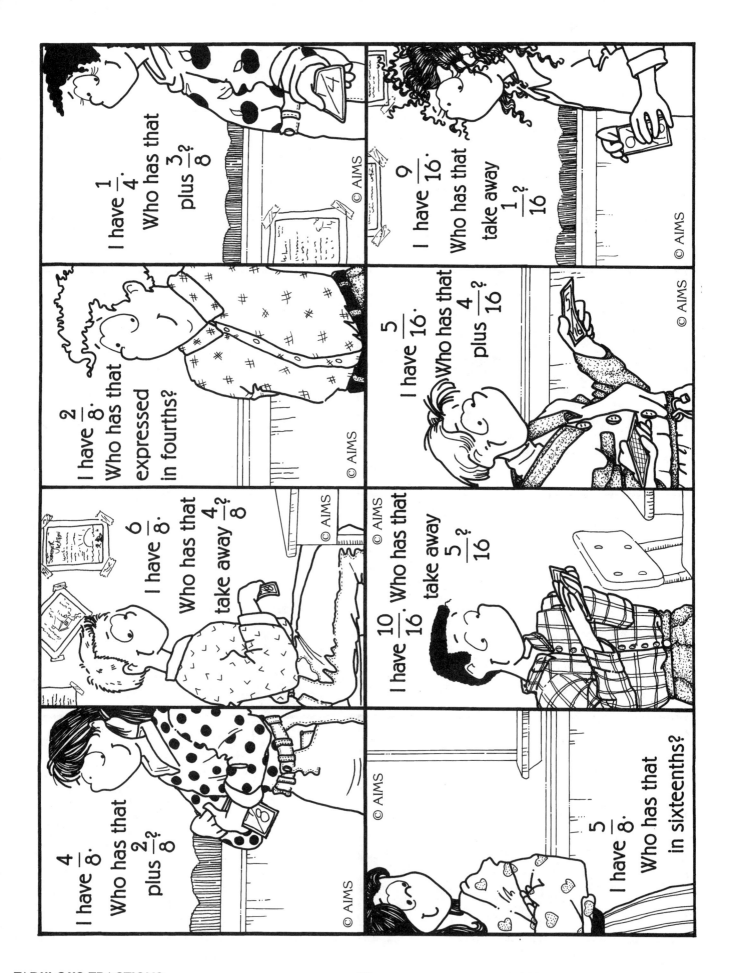

I have $\frac{1}{4}$.
Who has that plus $\frac{3}{8}$?

I have $\frac{9}{16}$.
Who has that take away $\frac{1}{16}$?

I have $\frac{2}{8}$.
Who has that expressed in fourths?

I have $\frac{5}{16}$.
Who has that plus $\frac{4}{16}$?

I have $\frac{6}{8}$.
Who has that take away $\frac{4}{8}$?

I have $\frac{10}{16}$. Who has that take away $\frac{5}{16}$?

I have $\frac{4}{8}$.
Who has that plus $\frac{2}{8}$?

I have $\frac{5}{8}$.
Who has that in sixteenths?

© AIMS

FABULOUS FRACTIONS

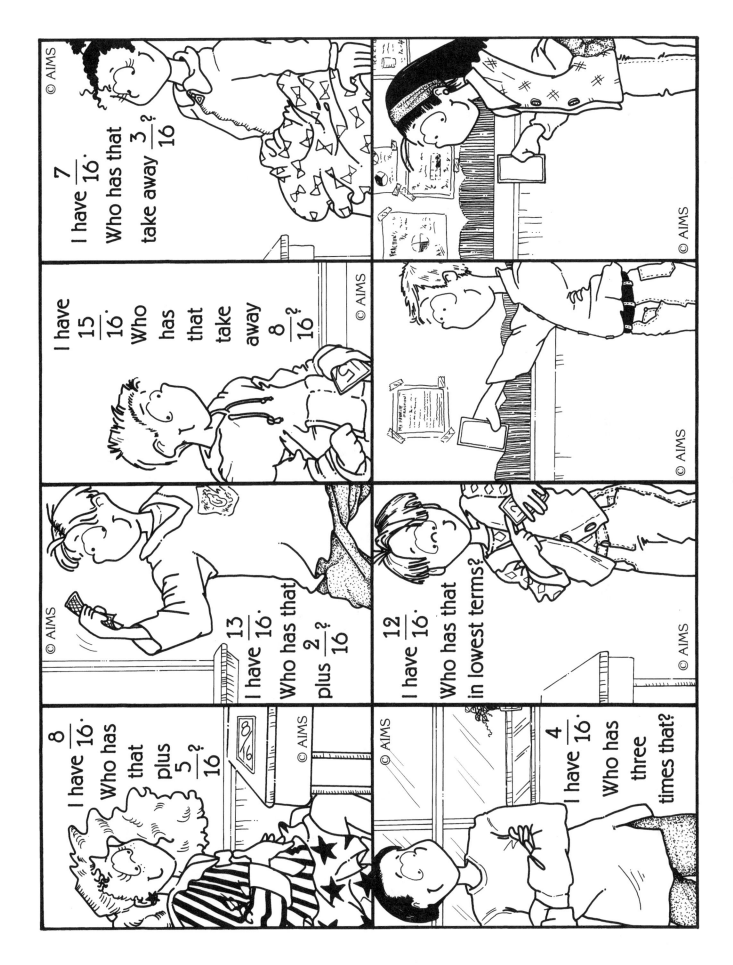

A Final Word About Fractions

Students need multiple ways of demonstrating what they know and understand about fractions. Included in each learning experience throughout this publication are ideas about learning goals and ways to gather evidence of student understanding along the way.

It is also appropriate to be thoughtful of various ways that students could share their knowledge and understanding of fractions as a culminating experience.

Fractions Evaluation Checklist
A list of fraction concepts drawn from activities is included in *Fabulous Fractions*.

Poster Proofs
A presentation with evidence and explanation is described in this publication and also includes a 4-point rubric for scoring.

Fraction Journal or Letter or Web Page
Consider encouraging students to design some kind of written dialogue to be shared with:
A member of your family
A teacher or student from another school
A friend who will be learning about fractions next year
A pen pal who lives far away
A politician or public servant interested in education
A high school or college professor interested in mathematics
An Internet user with similar interests

This reflective work could include the following:
1. What are three ideas you learned about fractions and why do you think they are important?
2. Which activity from *Fabulous Fractions* was the most difficult? Explain what was hard about it and what you learned from it.
3. Which activity was the most fun and how did it help you learn about fractions?

Topic
Fractions
   Equivalence

Learning Goals
- To recognize fractions in a variety of equivalent forms
- To be able to show the relationship of two unequal fractions using a variety of models and examples

Guiding Document
NCTM Standards 2000*
- *Develop understanding of fractions as parts of unit wholes, as parts of a collection, as locations on number lines, and as divisions of whole numbers*
- *Use models, benchmarks, and equivalent forms to judge the size of fractions*
- *Recognize and generate equivalent forms of commonly used fractions, decimals, and percents*
- *Work flexibly with fractions, decimals, and percents to solve problems*

Materials
For each student or pair of students
   one set of two unequal fractions selected from this list: (or of your own design)

$\frac{2}{3}$ and $\frac{3}{4}$

$\frac{2}{3}$ and $\frac{4}{5}$

$\frac{3}{5}$ and $\frac{2}{3}$

$\frac{5}{6}$ and $\frac{3}{4}$

$\frac{7}{8}$ and $\frac{3}{4}$

$\frac{5}{8}$ and $\frac{2}{3}$

$\frac{3}{4}$ and $\frac{7}{12}$

$\frac{5}{6}$ and $\frac{11}{12}$

$\frac{6}{10}$ and $\frac{4}{5}$

$\frac{6}{10}$ and $\frac{5}{8}$

chart paper
colored marking pens

Background Information
This activity is intended for use as an evaluation of student understanding of fraction concepts of equivalency, fair shares, relative size and symbolic representation of numerator and denominator. It is therefore assumed that considerable experience with these concepts using manipulatives and pictures has been provided for students prior to this one.

Management
1. If this activity is to serve as an evaluation experience, the teacher needs to determine ahead of time whether it is to be an independent or cooperative exercise. Both opportunities are described.
2. Make cards with two unequal fractions on each card. (See *Materials.*)

Procedure
1. Distribute to each student or pair of students a card on which are printed two unequal fractions, such as $\frac{2}{3}$ and $\frac{3}{4}$. Each student or pair of students receives a different pair of fractions.
2. Inform the students that the task is to design a large poster that illustrates and explains the relationship between the two given fractions using models, pictures, events, and explanations that clearly demonstrate that they understand how the two fractions are related.
3. Explain that they should use at least five of the models from class exploration and discussion and also to be innovative, creative, and artistic in showing their understanding of the meaning of fractions.

Evaluation
This experience has been designed to provide opportunities for students to share their understanding of equivalence and maximize their creative input using words, pictures, and symbols. It has potential to become an example of a performance assessment with a set of scoring rules for student and teacher evaluators. Both evidence and explanation are part of the assessment product.

Evidence of Learning

Since this activity could be a culminating assessment tool to gather evidence of understanding, it is appropriate to design a set of scoring rules to be shared with students ahead of time. One example is shared here, but it is important to recognize that scoring rules should be written with prior learning goals and lessons in mind.

Task

Design a poster that illustrates and explains how two unequal fractions are related. Use at least five models or illustrations that show understanding of equivalency, fair shares, relative size, and meaning of numerator and denominator.

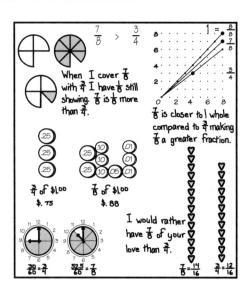

Scoring Rules (General)

4 Exceeds Expectations
3 Meets Expectations
2 Attempts to Meet Expectations, some errors
1 Minimal Attempt, many errors

Scoring Rules (Specific)

4 More than five different models or illustrations indicate accurate representation of the relationship of the two given fractions showing relative size, fair shares, and meaningful use of numerator and denominator and include an explanation of student's thinking. Student shows insight and creativity.

3 Five different models or illustrations accurately show the relationship between the two fractions. Pictures or models provide evidence of understanding of fair shares, relative size, and use of numerator and denominator. Student is able to explain his/her thinking.

2 Fewer than five models or illustrations are shown and pictures or models demonstrate partial understanding of the relationship of the two fractions, their relative size, and accurate use of numerator and denominator. Student is somewhat able to explain the thinking involved with few errors.

1 Fewer than three models or illustrations are shown and minimal understanding evident. Student is unable to provide adequate explanation of thinking. Many errors are evident.

Rubric for Scoring Posters	4 Points	3 Points	2 Points	1 Point
Number of models shown or illustrated	More than 5	5	4 or 3	2 or 1
Models and illustrations are accurate. Accurate models show relative size, fair shares and wholes, and meaningful use of numerator and denominator.	Models and illustrations are accurate and go beyond demonstrated models.	Models and illustrations are accurate.	Most models and illustrations are accurate with few errors.	Many errors are found in models and illustrations.
Explanations are accurate.	Explanations are accurate and includes discussion of student thinking. Shows insight and creativity.	Explanation is accurate and includes discussion of student thinking.	Explanation parrots instruction without indicating student thinking or understanding.	Explanation lacks understanding and includes errors or is inadequate.

* Reprinted with permission from *Principles and Standards for School Mathematics,* 2000 by the National Council of Teachers of Mathematics. All rights reserved.

Fraction Evaluation Check List

Student

Fraction Concept/Skill						
Recognizes and names fractions correctly as part of a counted set of objects						
Shows understanding of meaning of numerator and denominator						
Understands concept of fair shares						
Recognizes fractions as parts of a unit whole						
Use models and equivalent forms to judge the relative size of fractions						
Recognizes and names equivalent fractions						
Uses a model to show how fractions, decimals, and percents are related						
Understands the relative magnitude of decimal numbers						
Understands relative size of fractions as part of a linear unit						
Sequences correctly 5–8 unequal fractions on a number line from smallest to greatest						
Represents and interprets fractions in a circle or pie graph						
Uses visual models and equivalent forms to add and subtract commonly used fractions						
Demonstrates understanding of multiplication of fractions using an area model						
Shows understanding of division of fractions within a meaningful context of selected problems						
Shows and explains with confidence the relationship of two unequal fractions using a variety of models						

Fabulous Fractions Kits

Fraction Circle Model (transparent)

This set includes nine plastic circles divided into halves, thirds, fourths, fifths, sixths, eighths, tenths, twelfths, and one whole in eight transparent colors with storage box/work tray.

	#4170	$9.50

Fractional Transparencies

Colorful transparencies of the unit square as a model for multiplication of fractions are available for classroom use. One set is included with *Fabulous Fractions*.

Pkg. 5 Sets	#4148	$14.95

Fraction Pattern Blocks

Expand the use of pattern blocks by adding two new shapes representing one-fourth and one-twelfth of a hexagon. Thirty one-fourth and 60 one-twelfth shapes included.

Fraction Pattern Blocks 5mm (90 pieces)	#3031	$9.25

Plastic Pattern Blocks

Use these sets of 250 blocks, in six shapes and six colors to explore patterns, symmetry, linear and area measurement, fractions and problem solving.

Plastic Pattern Blocks 5mm (250 pieces)	#4250	$15.95

Who Has? Cards

Who Has? Fraction Cards require that students add and subtract like fractions and express fractions in equivalent terms.

	#4142	$6.95

Fraction/Equivalence Practice Game

Each card names a fraction in numerical and written form and shows a representation. Pairs consist of equivalent fractions in one variation and two fractions whose sum is one in the other.

	#4157	$5.95

Fraction Fringe Kit

A set of colored papers sharing a common linear measure that becomes a tool for comparing relative sizes of fractions and also for recognizing and naming equivalent fractions. Includes 20 sheets of seven different colors of paper and 80 sheets of black construction paper to complete 40 student sets.

	#4132	$4.95

The AIMS Program

AIMS is the acronym for "**A**ctivities **I**ntegrating **M**athematics and **S**cience." Such integration enriches learning and makes it meaningful and holistic. AIMS began as a project of Fresno Pacific University to integrate the study of mathematics and science in grades K-9, but has since expanded to include language arts, social studies, and other disciplines.

AIMS is a continuing program of the non-profit AIMS Education Foundation. It had its inception in a National Science Foundation funded program whose purpose was to explore the effectiveness of integrating mathematics and science. The project directors in cooperation with 80 elementary classroom teachers devoted two years to a thorough field-testing of the results and implications of integration.

The approach met with such positive results that the decision was made to launch a program to create instructional materials incorporating this concept. Despite the fact that thoughtful educators have long recommended an integrative approach, very little appropriate material was available in 1981 when the project began. A series of writing projects have ensued, and today the AIMS Education Foundation is committed to continue the creation of new integrated activities on a permanent basis.

The AIMS program is funded through the sale of books, products, and staff development workshops and through proceeds from the Foundation's endowment. All net income from program and products flows into a trust fund administered by the AIMS Education Foundation. Use of these funds is restricted to support of research, development, and publication of new materials. Writers donate all their rights to the Foundation to support its on-going program. No royalties are paid to the writers.

The rationale for integration lies in the fact that science, mathematics, language arts, social studies, etc., are integrally interwoven in the real world from which it follows that they should be similarly treated in the classroom where we are preparing students to live in that world. Teachers who use the AIMS program give enthusiastic endorsement to the effectiveness of this approach.

Science encompasses the art of questioning, investigating, hypothesizing, discovering, and communicating. Mathematics is the language that provides clarity, objectivity, and understanding. The language arts provide us powerful tools of communication. Many of the major contemporary societal issues stem from advancements in science and must be studied in the context of the social sciences. Therefore, it is timely that all of us take seriously a more holistic mode of educating our students. This goal motivates all who are associated with the AIMS Program. We invite you to join us in this effort.

Meaningful integration of knowledge is a major recommendation coming from the nation's professional science and mathematics associations. The American Association for the Advancement of Science in *Science for All Americans* strongly recommends the integration of mathematics, science, and technology. The National Council of Teachers of Mathematics places strong emphasis on applications of mathematics such as are found in science investigations. AIMS is fully aligned with these recommendations.

Extensive field testing of AIMS investigations confirms these beneficial results:

1. Mathematics becomes more meaningful, hence more useful, when it is applied to situations that interest students.
2. The extent to which science is studied and understood is increased, with a significant economy of time, when mathematics and science are integrated.
3. There is improved quality of learning and retention, supporting the thesis that learning that is meaningful and relevant is more effective.
4. Motivation and involvement are increased dramatically as students investigate real-world situations and participate actively in the process.

We invite you to become part of this classroom teacher movement by using an integrated approach to learning and sharing any suggestions you may have.

The AIMS Program welcomes you!

AIMS Education Foundation Programs

Practical proven strategies to improve student achievement

When you host an AIMS workshop for elementary and middle school educators, you will know your teachers are receiving effective usable training they can apply in their classrooms immediately.

Designed for teachers—AIMS Workshops:

- Correlate to your state standards;
- Address key topic areas, including math content, science content, problem solving, and process skills;
- Teach you how to use AIMS' effective hands-on approach;
- Provide practice of activity-based teaching;
- Address classroom management issues, higher-order thinking skills, and materials;
- Give you AIMS resources; and
- Offer college (graduate-level) credits for many courses.

Aligned to district and administrator needs—AIMS workshops offer:

- Flexible scheduling and grade span options;
- Custom (one-, two-, or three-day) workshops to meet specific schedule, topic and grade-span needs;
- Pre-packaged one-day workshops on most major topics—only $3900 for up to 30 participants (includes all materials and expenses);
- Prepackaged four- or five-day workshops for in-depth math and science training—only $12,300 for up to 30 participants (includes all materials and expenses);
- Sustained staff development, by scheduling workshops throughout the school year and including follow-up and assessment;
- Eligibility for funding under the Title I and Title II sections of No Child Left Behind; and

- Affordable professional development—save when you schedule consecutive-day workshops.

University Credit—Correspondence Courses

AIMS offers correspondence courses through a partnership with Fresno Pacific University.

- Convenient distance-learning courses—you study at your own pace and schedule. No computer or Internet access required!

The tuition for each three-semester unit graduate-level course is $264 plus a materials fee.

The AIMS Instructional Leadership Program

This is an AIMS staff-development program seeking to prepare facilitators for leadership roles in science/math education in their home districts or regions. Upon successful completion of the program, trained facilitators become members of the AIMS Instructional Leadership Network, qualified to conduct AIMS workshops, teach AIMS in-service courses for college credit, and serve as AIMS consultants. Intensive training is provided in mathematics, science, process and thinking skills, workshop management, and other relevant topics.

Introducing AIMS Science Core Curriculum

Developed to meet 100% of your state's standards, AIMS' Science Core Curriculum gives students the opportunity to build content knowledge, thinking skills, and fundamental science processes.

- *Each* grade specific module has been developed to extend the AIMS approach to full-year science programs.
- *Each* standards-based module includes math, reading, hands-on investigations, and assessments.

Like all AIMS resources, these core modules are able to serve students at all stages of readiness, making these a great value across the grades served in your school.

For current information regarding the programs described above, please complete the following form and mail it to: P.O. Box 8120, Fresno, CA 93747.

Information Request

Please send current information on the items checked:

_____ *Basic Information Packet* on AIMS materials   _____ Hosting information for AIMS workshops
_____ *AIMS Instructional Leadership Program*   _____ AIMS Science Core Curriculum

Name _____   Phone _____

Address_____
          Street   City   State   Zip

© 2004 AIMS Education Foundation

Magazine

YOUR K-9 MATH AND SCIENCE
CLASSROOM ACTIVITIES RESOURCE

The AIMS Magazine is your source for standards-based, hands-on math and science investigations. Each issue is filled with teacher-friendly, ready-to-use activities that engage students in meaningful learning.

- *Four issues each year (fall, winter, spring, and summer).*

Current issue is shipped with all past issues within that volume.

1820	Volume XX	2005-2006	$19.95
1821	Volume XXI	2006-2007	$19.95
1822	Volume XXII	2007-2008	$19.95

Two-Volume Combination
| M20507 | Volumes XX & XXI | 2005-2007 | $34.95 |
| M20608 | Volumes XXI & XXII | 2006-2008 | $34.95 |

Back Volumes Available
Complete volumes available for purchase:

1802	Volume II	1987-1988	$19.95
1804	Volume IV	1989-1990	$19.95
1805	Volume V	1990-1991	$19.95
1807	Volume VII	1992-1993	$19.95
1808	Volume VIII	1993-1994	$19.95
1809	Volume IX	1994-1995	$19.95
1810	Volume X	1995-1996	$19.95
1811	Volume XI	1996-1997	$19.95
1812	Volume XII	1997-1998	$19.95
1813	Volume XIII	1998-1999	$19.95
1814	Volume XIV	1999-2000	$19.95
1815	Volume XV	2000-2001	$19.95
1816	Volume XVI	2001-2002	$19.95
1817	Volume XVII	2002-2003	$19.95
1818	Volume XVIII	2003-2004	$19.95
1819	Volume XIX	2004-2005	$35.00

Volumes II to XIX include 10 issues.

Call 1.888.733.2467 or go to www.aimsedu.org

Subscribe to the AIMS Magazine

$19.95 a year!

AIMS Magazine is published four times a year.

Subscriptions ordered at any time will receive all the issues for that year.

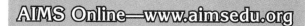

AIMS Online—www.aimsedu.org

To see all that AIMS has to offer, check us out on the Internet at www.aimsedu.org. At our website you can search our activities database; preview and purchase individual AIMS activities; learn about core curriculum, college courses, and workshops; buy manipulatives and other classroom resources; and download free resources including articles, puzzles, and sample AIMS activities.

AIMS News
While visiting the AIMS website, sign up for AIMS News, our FREE e-mail newsletter. You'll get the latest information on what's new at AIMS including:

- New publications;
- New core curriculum modules; and
- New materials.

Sign up today!

AIMS Program Publications

Actions with Fractions, 4-9
Awesome Addition and Super Subtraction, 2-3
Bats Incredible! 2-4
Brick Layers II, 4-9
Chemistry Matters, 4-7
Counting on Coins, K-2
Cycles of Knowing and Growing, 1-3
Crazy about Cotton, 3-7
Critters, 2-5
Electrical Connections, 4-9
Exploring Environments, K-6
Fabulous Fractions, 3-6
Fall into Math and Science, K-1
Field Detectives, 3-6
Finding Your Bearings, 4-9
Floaters and Sinkers, 5-9
From Head to Toe, 5-9
Fun with Foods, 5-9
Glide into Winter with Math and Science, K-1
Gravity Rules! 5-12
Hardhatting in a Geo-World, 3-5
It's About Time, K-2
It Must Be A Bird, Pre-K-2
Jaw Breakers and Heart Thumpers, 3-5
Looking at Geometry, 6-9
Looking at Lines, 6-9
Machine Shop, 5-9
Magnificent Microworld Adventures, 5-9
Marvelous Multiplication and Dazzling Division, 4-5
Math + Science, A Solution, 5-9
Mostly Magnets, 2-8
Movie Math Mania, 6-9
Multiplication the Algebra Way, 6-8
Off the Wall Science, 3-9
Out of This World, 4-8
Paper Square Geometry:
    The Mathematics of Origami, 5-12
Puzzle Play, 4-8
Pieces and Patterns, 5-9
Popping With Power, 3-5
Positive vs. Negative, 6-9
Primarily Bears, K-6
Primarily Earth, K-3
Primarily Physics, K-3
Primarily Plants, K-3

Problem Solving: Just for the Fun of It! 4-9
Problem Solving: Just for the Fun of It! Book Two, 4-9
Proportional Reasoning, 6-9
Ray's Reflections, 4-8
Sense-Able Science, K-1
Soap Films and Bubbles, 4-9
Solve It! K-1: Problem-Solving Strategies, K-1
Solve It! 2nd: Problem-Solving Strategies, 2
Solve It! 3rd: Problem-Solving Strategies, 3
Solve It! 4th: Problem-Solving Strategies, 4
Solve It! 5th: Problem-Solving Strategies, 5
Spatial Visualization, 4-9
Spills and Ripples, 5-12
Spring into Math and Science, K-1
The Amazing Circle, 4-9
The Budding Botanist, 3-6
The Sky's the Limit, 5-9
Through the Eyes of the Explorers, 5-9
Under Construction, K-2
Water Precious Water, 2-6
Weather Sense: Temperature, Air Pressure, and Wind, 4-5
Weather Sense: Moisture, 4-5
Winter Wonders, K-2

Spanish Supplements*
Fall Into Math and Science, K-1
Glide Into Winter with Math and Science, K-1
Mostly Magnets, 2-8
Pieces and Patterns, 5-9
Primarily Bears, K-6
Primarily Physics, K-3
Sense-Able Science, K-1
Spring Into Math and Science, K-1

* Spanish supplements are only available as downloads from the
  AIMS website. The supplements contain only the student pages
  in Spanish; you will need the English version of the book for the
  teacher's text.

Spanish Edition
Constructores II: Ingeniería Creativa Con Construcciones
    LEGO® 4-9
    The entire book is written in Spanish. English pages not included.

Other Publications
Historical Connections in Mathematics, Vol. I, 5-9
Historical Connections in Mathematics, Vol. II, 5-9
Historical Connections in Mathematics, Vol. III, 5-9
Mathematicians are People, Too
Mathematicians are People, Too, Vol. II
What's Next, Volume 1, 4-12
What's Next, Volume 2, 4-12
What's Next, Volume 3, 4-12

For further information write to:
AIMS Education Foundation • P.O. Box 8120 • Fresno, California 93747-8120
www.aimsedu.org • 559.255.6396 (fax) • 888.733.2467 (toll free)

© 2004 AIMS Education Foundation

Duplication Rights

Standard Duplication Rights

Purchasers of AIMS activities (individually or in books and magazines) may make up to 200 copies of any portion of the purchased activities, provided these copies will be used for educational purposes and only at one school site.

Workshop or conference presenters may make one copy of a purchased activity for each participant, with a limit of five activities per workshop or conference session.

Standard duplication rights apply to activities received at workshops, free sample activities provided by AIMS, and activities received by conference participants.

All copies must bear the AIMS Education Foundation copyright information.

Unlimited Duplication Rights

To ensure compliance with copyright regulations, AIMS users may upgrade from standard to unlimited duplication rights. Such rights permit unlimited duplication of purchased activities (including revisions) for use at a given school site.

Activities received at workshops are eligible for upgrade from standard to unlimited duplication rights.

Free sample activities and activities received as a conference participant are not eligible for upgrade from standard to unlimited duplication rights.

Upgrade Fees

The fees for upgrading from standard to unlimited duplication rights are:
- $5 per activity per site,
- $25 per book per site, and
- $10 per magazine issue per site.

The cost of upgrading is shown in the following examples:
- activity: 5 activities x 5 sites x $5 = $125
- book: 10 books x 5 sites x $25 = $1250
- magazine issue: 1 issue x 5 sites x $10 = $50

Purchasing Unlimited Duplication Rights

To purchase unlimited duplication rights, please provide us the following:
1. The name of the individual responsible for coordinating the purchase of duplication rights.
2. The title of each book, activity, and magazine issue to be covered.
3. The number of school sites and name of each site for which rights are being purchased.
4. Payment (check, purchase order, credit card)

Requested duplication rights are automatically authorized with payment. The individual responsible for coordinating the purchase of duplication rights will be sent a certificate verifying the purchase.

Internet Use

Permission to make AIMS activities available on the Internet is determined on a case-by-case basis.

• P. O. Box 8120, Fresno, CA 93747-8120 •
• permissions@aimsedu.org • www.aimsedu.org •
• 559.255.6396 (fax) • 888.733.2467 (toll free) •